Content

Introduction   1

Level 1 Cross-cutting (...for safe chainsaw operation – harvest trees manually)   3
Professional attitude
Workplace safety   5
     Risk assessment for chainsaw users   5
Dangerous trees   7
Occupational hazards   8
Personal protection equipment   9
Basic safety   10
     Starting a chainsaw   13
Kick-back   15
Safety warning signs used throughout the NSW timber industry   19
Power head maintenance   20
     Daily service   21
     Fortnightly service   22
     Guide bar maintenance   23
     Chainsaw power head trouble-shooting chart   24
The cutting attachment   26
     Sprockets   26
     Guide bar   28
Sawchain   30
     Chain components   30
     Cutters   30
     Reduced vibration chain   32
Sawchain sharpening   33
     Depth gauge setting   34
     'Breaking-in' a new sawchain   35
     Chain tension   35
     Hand filing   36
Sawchain design   39
Cross-cutting sequence   41
     Basic principles of cross-cutting   41
     Assessment of internal stresses in fallen timber   42
     Types of binds   42
         Top bind   42
         Top bind using a wedge   42
         Bottom bind   42
         Side bind   43
     Log trap   44
     Wind blow   45
     Limbing   46
         Limbing small to medium-sized conifers   47
         Limbing large trees   48
Butt trimming   49
     Basic principles   49

Level 2 Simple tree felling
(Intermediate competence of safe chainsaw operation – harvest trees manually)   51
Theory of felling   52
     Importance of directional felling   53
     Considerations before felling each tree   53
Preparation at each tree prior to felling   55
     Clean around base of tree   55
     Prepare escape route   56

Theory of simple tree felling   58
   Scarf   58
   Standard scarf   59
   Features of a scarf   59
   Technique for cutting the scarf   60
   Other types of scarf   61
      Humbolt scarf   61
      V scarf   61
      Box scarf   61
      90° scarf   61
   Size of opening   62
   Cuts meet exactly   62
   Line of scarf is horizontal   62
   Back cut   63
   Holding wood (hingewood)   64
Wedges   65
   Types   65
   When used   65
   Using a wedge   65

Level 3 Problem tree felling
(Advanced competence of safe chainsaw operation – harvest trees manually)   67
Problem tree felling techniques   68
   Tree with side lean   68
      Uneven holding wood   68
      Uneven holding wood with wedges   68
      Uneven holding wood with plunge side cuts   69
   Tree with forward lean   70
      Technique No.1   70
      Technique No.2   70
   Small tree with the use of a wedge or felling bar   71
   Tree diameter over twice guide bar length   72
Double leader   73
Felling 'dangerous' trees   74
   Defective trees   74
   Snags (stags)   74
   Felling defective trees   75
   Wind blow   76
   Manual felling hung-up trees   77
Removal of tree lying across road/track   77
Machine assisted manual tree felling   77
   Line pull   78
   Line guide   79
Pushing tree over with a crawler tractor – dozer blade   80
Tree jacking   81

Competencies for safe chainsaw operation – Forest and Forest Products Industry Training Package   55
Level 1   84
   FPIC2007A Maintain chainsaws   84
   FPIH2001A Trim and cross-cut felled trees – Production   85
   FPIH2003A Harvest trees manually – Basic   89
Level 2   93
   FPIH3020A Harvest trees manually – Intermediate   93
Level 3   97
   FPIH3041A Harvest trees manually – Advanced   97

Additional reference material   101

Introduction

During the decades prior to 1990, NSW timber industry workers suffered horrific injuries and some times death due to chainsaw operation. Timber workers were experiencing cuts from revolving sawchains when a chainsaw 'kick-back' occurred, or were killed by falling trees or dislodged limbs due to unsafe felling techniques.

'Safe System of Work' for chainsaw operation was developed and introduced to the timber industry in the late 1970s and early 1980s. Since then the frequency and severity of chainsaw-related incidents have steadily declined, to a point where during the financial year 1994–95, there were no chainsaw operation fatalities recorded in forests managed by State Forests of NSW.

The low frequency of chainsaw-related incidents remained until the period June 2000 to November 2001 where seven fatalities were recorded.

State Forests of NSW is directly concerned about the safety and welfare of its own employees and all timber workers who use chainsaws in the course of their work. This manual is designed primarily for their use.

However the manual will also provide guidance on safe chainsaw operation to the wider community.

This 6th edition upgrades the older editions with the inclusion of sections dealing with:

- Workplace risk assessment for chainsaw users
- Management of dangerous trees
- Upgraded information regarding sawchain components and sharpening practices
- Introduction of the new NSW Timber Industry Safety Warning Signs
- Machine assisted manual tree felling
    - Line pull
    - Line guide
- Tree jacking
- National competencies for chainsaw operation:
    Level 1
    FPIC2007A Maintain chainsaws
    FPIH2001A Trim and cross-cut felled trees – Production
    FPIH2003A Harvest trees manually – Basic
    Level 2
    FPIH3020A Harvest trees manually – Intermediate
    Level 3
    FPIH3041A Harvest trees manually – Advanced

Level 1
Cross-cutting

(Basic competence for safe chainsaw operation – harvest trees manually)

Professional attitude

It is essential that a chainsaw operator develops a professional attitude towards all aspects of timber felling.

Factors that influence professional attitude are:

- Cares for their equipment i.e. carries out regular chainsaw maintenance including engine tuning and minor repairs.
- Can confidently assess a tree they intend to fell regarding: tree's natural lean, presence of dangerous limbs, defects in tree, and the influence of any wind upon the felling operation.
- Can fell a tree in the 'desired direction of fall'.
- Has a keen sense of safety in relation to themselves, other people and their personal equipment.
- Has a sense of responsibility towards the environment and the final condition of the tree being felled.

Features that help to make a competent faller:

- Forward planning
- Steady work pace
- Concentration at all times
- The use of sound, low risk techniques

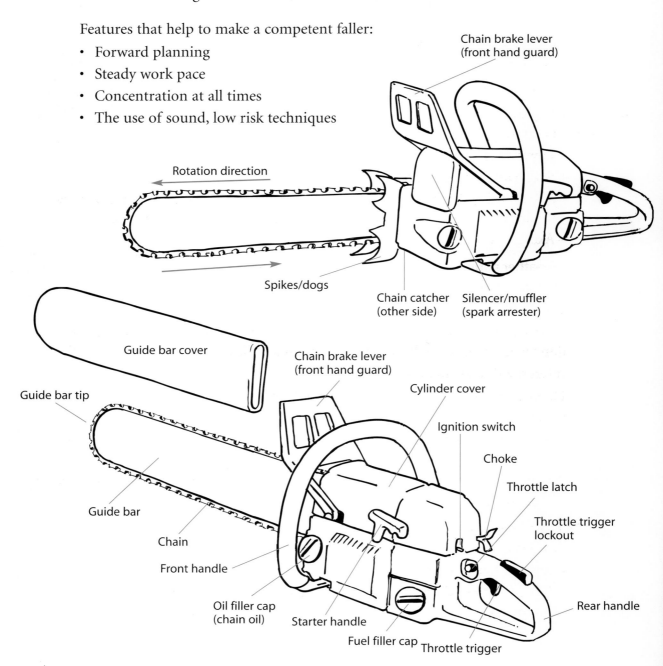

Chain brake lever (front hand guard)

Rotation direction

Spikes/dogs

Chain catcher (other side)

Silencer/muffler (spark arrester)

Guide bar cover

Guide bar tip

Chain brake lever (front hand guard)

Cylinder cover

Ignition switch

Choke

Throttle latch

Throttle trigger lockout

Guide bar

Chain

Front handle

Oil filler cap (chain oil)

Starter handle

Fuel filler cap

Throttle trigger

Rear handle

Workplace safety

Risk assessment for chainsaw users

Before starting your chainsaw to fell a tree or cross-cut a limb, it is vital that you think about what you are about to do before you do it.

Risk assessment is a process of thinking through what you are about to do to ensure that every aspect is covered.

Consider the following:

Your person

- Are you wearing the right Personal Protection Equipment (PPE)?
  - Safety hat
  - Ear protection (muffs or ear plugs)
  - Eye protection (visor or safety glasses)
  - Strong work boots (high ankle support; deep non-slip sole, safety-toe capped is preferred)
  - Cut-resistant trousers or chaps
  - High-visibility vest or shirt
  - Close-fitting leather gloves

Your equipment

- Chainsaw
  - Powerhead well maintained
  - Sawchain sharpened and correctly tensioned
  - Full of fuel and bar oil (must have sufficient fuel to complete the felling operation – it may be unsafe to stop the cutting sequence to refuel, leaving a partially cut tree)
  - Axe and wedges must be immediately to hand

The weather at time of chainsaw operation

- Do not attempt to fell a tree in bad weather, especially high winds

The tree's/limb's immediate surrounds

- Presence of broken limbs hanging (widow makers) in trees in close proximity i.e. don't work within the drop zone of a hanging broken limb
- Intergrowth with adjoining trees
- Hung-up tree/s in contact with tree to be felled
- Climbing vines in contact with tree to be felled
- Presence of other smaller trees or under growth that may be a hazard during the cutting process
- Open space into which the tree can be felled i.e. don't fell tree into another standing tree (remove the other tree first)

The tree to be felled

- Condition of tree
  - Is it a dangerous tree?
  - Is the felling of the tree within the faller's capacity to fell it safely and competently?

- Desired direction of fall
  - Safe area into which to fell the tree
  - Tree not to interfere with prohibited area (boundary, buffer zone, etc)

Escape route
- Appropriate route (45° back away from desired direction of fall) to be free of obstacles for at least 4 or more metres
- Prepare most suitable escape route

Sequence of cuts
- Appropriate to tree being felled and its desired direction of fall

Before starting chainsaw – final check!!
- Presence of any person or machinery within 2 tree lengths?
- Desired direction of fall?
- Sequence of cuts to be used?
- What side of tree you will be at when putting in the release cut?
- Escape route?
- Fuel OK? Axe and wedge immediately to hand?

> *Remember – If you can't fell the tree safely – Don't!*
>
> *Look up and live*

Dangerous trees

Any tree that can't be felled safely by the chainsaw operator can be considered to be 'dangerous'. The danger may come from the tree itself, the tree's immediate surroundings, or the weather conditions prevailing at the time of felling.

It is vital for chainsaw operators to assess the condition of a tree and its environment **before** any attempt is made to fell it.

Typical examples of dangerous trees

- Tree with heavy decay or fire scarring
- Tree which is dead or partially dead
- Tree which is very brittle or hollow trunk
- Tree which has broken limbs hanging in its crown
- Tree whose natural lean is away from the desired direction of fall
- Tree with excessive lean
- Tree which is hung-up or has a hung-up tree resting in it
- Tree which is interlocked with adjoining trees

Typical examples of conditions that make the felling of a tree dangerous

- Tree felling
  - in stormy or windy weather
  - at night
  - on a bush fire front, particularly if the tree is alight.

Competence

Manual tree felling of **DANGEROUS TREES** can only be undertaken by professional chainsaw operators who hold accreditation for:

- Harvest Trees Manually, Advanced – Level 3 FPIH3041A
- Forest & Harvesting Products, Industry Training Package – FP119
- or equivalent

See section dealing with manual tree felling with mechanical assistance.

Occupational hazards

Falling limbs and branches
- Always wear safety helmet.
- Do not enter felling area until adjacent trees have settled.
- Keep a sharp watch for hanging limbs etc.

Eye injuries
- Wear mesh visor attached to safety helmet or safety glasses.

Industrial deafness
- Hearing can be seriously impaired by chainsaw noise.
- Wear earmuffs for protection. Appropriate ear plugs can be worn as an alternative.
- Remember a hearing aid will not overcome high frequency hearing loss.

Note: It is important that hearing protection devices have sufficient noise reduction capacity. For technical advice refer to the NSW WorkCover Authority, or similar organisation.

Foot injuries
- Wear heavy work boots with a deep patterned sole and adequate ankle support. Safety boots with steel toe-caps are preferred.

Reynaud's phenomenon
- 'White Fingers'. This mainly occurs in cold climates. Initially a tingling sensation occurs in the tips of the fingers, finally becoming white and numb.
- Keep hands warm and ensure the saw's anti-vibration mounts are in good condition.

Back injuries
- Use correct manual handling techniques at all times.
- Seek assistance when moving heavy or awkward objects.

Kick-back
- Inspect chain brake regularly. Do not operate saw if brake is not functioning correctly.
- Use reduced kick-back chain.
- Sharpen sawchain to makers' recommendations.

Environment
- Avoid using a chainsaw in wet or windy conditions.
- Watch for hidden stump holes and abandoned mine shafts.
- Keep fire-fighting equipment handy, especially during summer months.

Safety distance
- Keep at least twice the length of the tree being felled between fallers.
- Use warning signs when felling near roads or tracks.

Hand tools
- Keep all hand tools correctly sharpened and cutting edge covered when not in use.
- Replace damaged handles.
- Do not use wedges with burred heads.

Personal protection equipment

- The following items of equipment are considered essential for a timber faller:
- Safety helmet
- Ear muffs or plugs having sufficient attenuation
- Visor or safety glasses
- Strong work boots (steel toe-cap preferred) with strong ankle support and a deep non-slip tread.
- Reasonably close-fitting clothes
- Cut-resistant trousers or chaps
- Sharp axe
- Wedges
- High-visibility vest/shirt (production felling)
- Close-fitting gloves (optional)
- Approved fuel and oil containers
- Tool pouch and belt
- Appropriate chainsaw maintenance tools:
  - combination spanner
  - chain sharpening files (both flat and round)
  - chain sharpening angle gauge
  - depth gauge setter
  - spare air filter and spark plug.

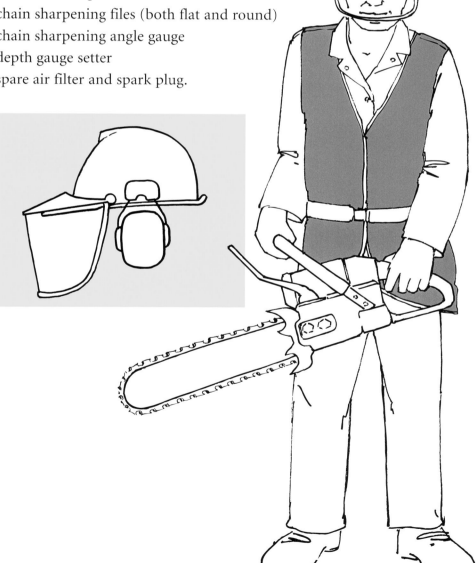

Basic safety

- Before attempting to use your chainsaw, thoroughly read the owner's manual.
- Chainsawing is a one person operation. Your best defence against accidents is to use correct techniques in chainsaw operation.
- A chainsaw operator should be suitably dressed before attempting any cross-cutting or tree felling.
(See section on personal equipment.)

A chainsaw in the hands of an incompetent person can be very dangerous

When all else fails read the instructions

It is important that your chainsaw is using petrol of the correct fuel/oil mixture. See your owner's manual.

State Forests recommends a fuel/oil mixture of 25:1 (air cooled 2 stroke oil).

Some smaller chainsaws require an oil mixture of 50:1.

- Always stop engine before refuelling.
- Don't smoke when handling fuel.
- Don't start the saw at the place of refuelling.

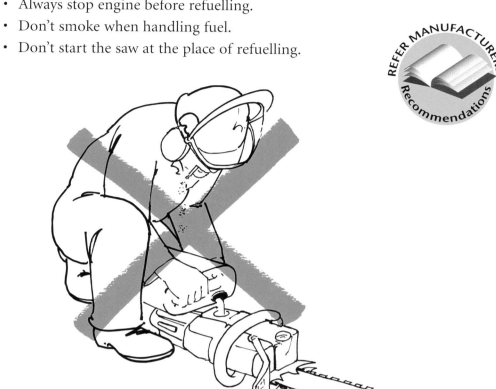

Don't smoke when refuelling.

Don't start the saw at the place of refuelling

When cutting, hold saw firmly with both hands and with thumb locked around front handle. Do not start cutting until you have a clear place in which to stand, a firm footing and a safe exit from falling timber or rolling logs.

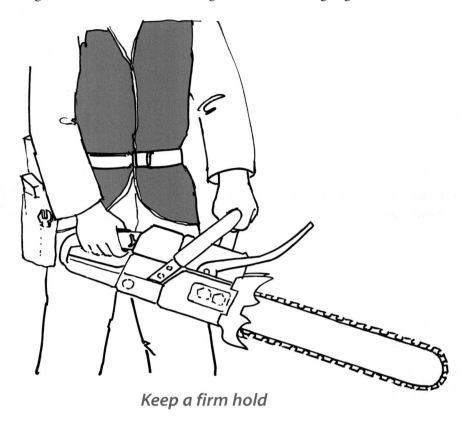

Keep a firm hold

Never attempt to cut with a loose or dull chain.
For optimum performance, it is essential that the chain be kept sharp.
(See section on Chain sharpening.)

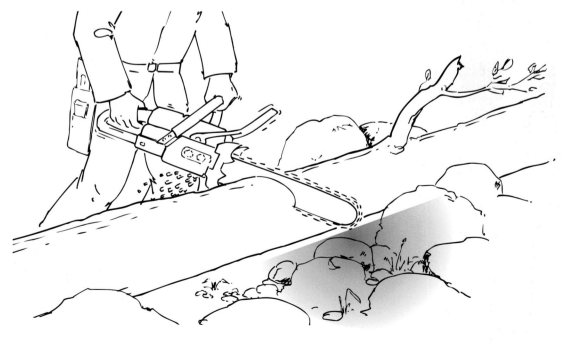

Keep the chain away from dirt or rocks

Starting a chainsaw

The safest way of starting a chainsaw is by placing saw on ground and starting it from there.

Always start the saw by yourself, away from any other person.

Starting saw on ground

Start the saw on the ground, without help.

1. Apply chain brake.
2. Place saw on ground.
3. Clear away any obstacles, particularly near tip of guide bar.
4. Place the right foot through the rear handle and left hand on the front handle.
5. Pull the starter rope with the right hand.

Note: Chain brake should be engaged before starting saw.

Starting saw off ground

1. Grip the front handle with left hand, keeping arm straight.
2. Grip rear handle between knees at the angle shown in the diagram.
3. Use right hand to pull start rope.
4. Maintain straight back, look straight ahead.

Do not drop start

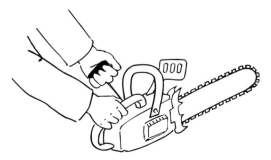

Starting a small saw

- Always carry the saw with the engine stopped, or chain brake applied.
- Don't work in the forest by yourself.
- Avoid using a chainsaw when you are tired.
- Don't attempt to touch or try to stop a moving chain with your hand.
- Ensure chain is stationary before moving your body position i.e. moving between cuts.

Keep alert!

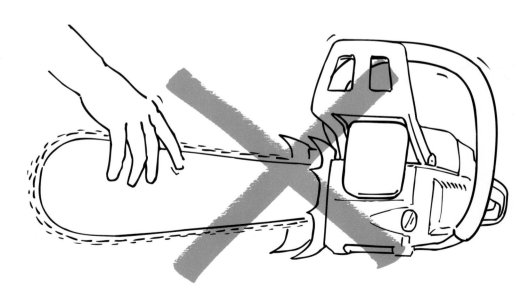

Don't touch a moving chain

Kick-back

Kick-back is one of the most common causes of chainsaw accidents. It occurs when a moving chain in the upper quadrant on the nose of guide bar contacts an obstacle, or becomes pinched, and rather than cutting through it, the guide bar moves upwards and backwards in an uncontrolled arc.

The guide bar can kick-back when:

1. Too much of the cutter bites into the wood and cannot sever it,
   i.e the noses of the cutters are more exposed because the:
   • depth gauges are too low
   • depth gauges are not rounded causing them to bury into the wood.

2. An obstacle strikes the front of the depth gauge or cutter. When the cutter hits an obstruction it cannot cut, an opposing force is delivered to the guide bar. The bar is thrown out of the cut (backwards and upwards) and can hit the operator if he/she is in line with the bar when this occurs (lacerated left hands are quite common as often when a kick-back occurs the operator loses their grip).

Speed of flight of the guide bar can approach 80 km/h – much faster than a normal person's reaction time.

Common kick-back situations

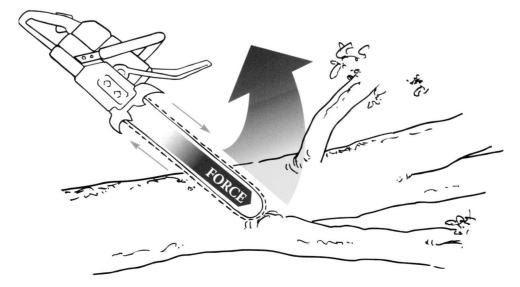

Time taken for guide bar to reach your face following kick-back

Automatic chain brake – 6/100 sec

Standard chain brake – 10/100 sec

Time taken to reach face – 15/100 sec

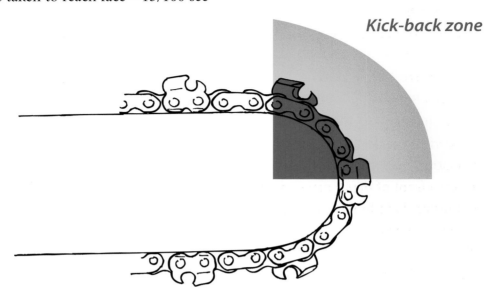

Kick-back (upper quadrant) danger zone

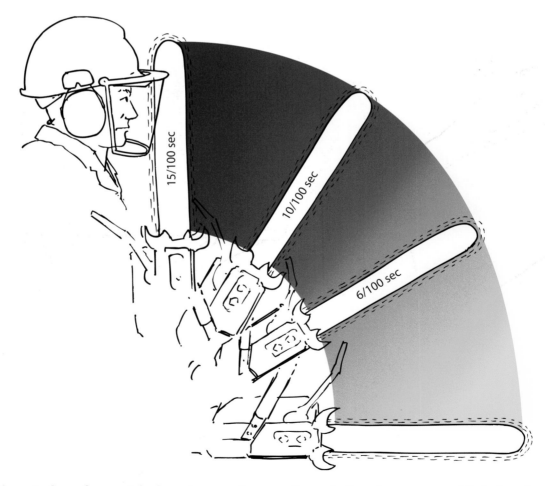

Time taken for guide bar to reach your face following severe kick-back

Always be on constant guard against kick-back

How to help reduce kick-back

- Maintain a firm grip (good footing, keep chainsaw close to body, straight wrist and thumb behind front handle).
- Cut at peak revs (more chance of cutting through an obstruction).
- Be conscious of where the nose of the bar is at all times.
- Use correct boring techniques.
- Avoid limbing with upper section of bar nose.
- Sharpen chain correctly.
- Tension chain correctly.
- Correct depth gauge setting.
- Keep front of depth gauges well rounded.
- Ensure chain brake is functioning correctly.
- Only use reduced kick-back chain.

Note: The width of guide bar relates directly to the potential for kick-back. The greater the nose radius, the greater the potential for kick-back.

Beware of kick-back!

Chainsaw's natural reaction when cutting wood

Cutting on top of log

Saw tends to pull in

Cutting underneath log

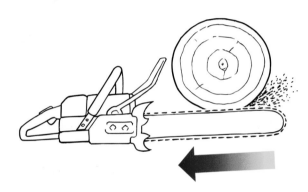

Saw tends to push back

Boring directly into log

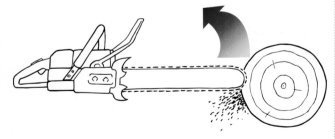

*Saw tends to kick-back
backwards and upwards*

Techniques in minimising chainsaw's reaction (particularly kick-back) when beginning a boring cut.

Starting on top of log

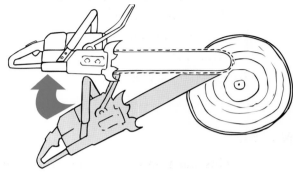

Starting in middle of log

1. Commence cut with the top of guide bar until the depth of the kerf is about the same as the width of the bar. This will serve to guide the bar, effectively eliminating the risk of kick-back.

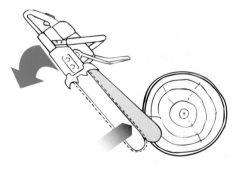

2. Next, align the saw in the direction in which the recess is to be cut.

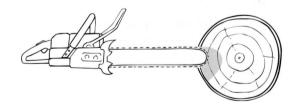

3. With the saw at full throttle, insert the guide bar in the trunk. If possible, support the saw against your legs.

Safety warning signs used throughout the NSW timber industry

- Warning signs to be placed on all road entry points leading to the active tree felling (harvesting) area.
- The placement of the warning signs will define the perimeter of the active tree felling area.
- Warning signs to be placed as per the Harvesting Plan or Site Safety Plan.

Note: The black and yellow triangular warning sign 'Tree Felling in Operation' is no longer used.

'No Entry'

- This warning sign may be used in any circumstance where there is an imminent hazard for the road user.
- When tree felling within two tree lengths of a road, one sign must be placed either end of the operation at a safe distance from the activity.
- Each warning sign must be accompanied by a physical barrier across the road to prevent vehicles passing the road closure point. Safety tape or vehicles are acceptable as a physical closure (barrier). Barriers (such as a log) must not prevent emergency access (such as ambulances or fire-fighting equipment).
- Warning signs and barriers must be erected by the operator before commencement of operations.
- Signs and barriers must only remain in place for the reasonable period that the hazard exists.
- This warning sign can also be used in emergency situations such as vehicle accidents and thus should be carried in all vehicles used in the timber industry.
- Authorised persons may progress beyond a road closure point only after receiving prior approval to do so from the person supervising the hazardous situation.

'Logging Machinery On Road'

- One warning sign must be placed either side of the following activities (operations):
- Building a log stack by a 'forwarder'
- Loading trucks
- Harvesting plant is on the road formation, log dump or landing.

Note: This warning sign is not required for log truck transit.

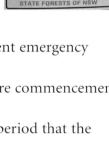

'Log Trucks Entering'

Warning signs must be erected by at major road intersections as directed by the Forests Practices Code and as identified in the Site Safety Plan prior to commencement of operations.

Power head maintenance

Regular maintenance of the chainsaw is essential to ensure a relatively trouble-free life.

It is the operator's responsibility to carry out a 'daily service' on their saw at least once a day. The most appropriate time is before using it. Also, a 'fortnightly service' should be done once during each fortnight, e.g. first thing every second Friday.

The right attitude towards servicing the chainsaw is important!

Things like:

Frequency
- Servicing on time.

Conscientious approach
- Willingness to look closely into all aspects of servicing.

Cleanliness
- Keep utensils used for handling of fuel and oil clean.
- Keep the saw free from accumulation of saw dust/dirt etc, particularly around the clutch/sprocket area and the engine's cooling fans.

Report
- Any deficiencies, defects, etc. promptly; or
- If the saw is privately owned, repair the saw the moment it becomes defective. Don't operate the saw if any of its components become defective, particularly safety components, e.g. dull chain, chain brake, anti-vibration mounts, etc.

The right attitude is important e.g. taking the trouble to ensure that the air filter is cleaned before starting work.

Daily service (frequent service)

'Take time to read and understand the manufacturer's recommendations.'

Air filter

- When required, remove and clean.
- Wash in chainsaw petrol/oil mix (from an environmental point of view, it is better to wash the air filter in soapy water).
- Refer to manufacturer's manuals for washing medium.

REFER MANUFACTURERS Recommendations

Chain/guide bar

- Remove chain and inspect bar.
- Clean out groove, remove any burrs.
- Clean oil holes.
- Sprocket nose
  - clean out debris
  - ensure sprocket rotates
  - grease, if appropriate
  - reverse.
- Install chain and sharpen. It may be necessary to sharpen the chain several times during the day.
- Tension chain correctly.

Chain brake

- Thoroughly clean, particularly around brake band and operating mechanism.
- Ensure correct operation.

Top up fuel and oil before starting work

Clean

- Thoroughly clean saw, pay particular attention to cooling fins.

Loose screws/nuts

- Check screws/nuts for tightness.

Petrol/oil ratio

- Refer to manufacturer's recommendations.
- If using oil, other than manufacturer's oil, it is recommended that a 25:1 fuel:oil ratio is used i.e. 200 ml of air cooled 2 stroke oil to 5 L of unleaded petrol.

Note: Do not use 2 stroke water cooled oil.

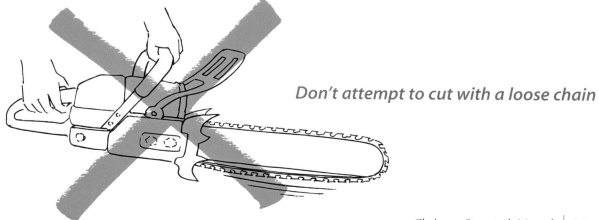

Don't attempt to cut with a loose chain

Fortnightly service (periodic service)

Air filter
- Remove and check for damage, clean or replace as necessary.

Spark plugs
- Remove, clean and adjust gap.

Fuel system
- Filter – check.
- Fuel tank – wash out accumulated saw dust with petrol/oil mix.

Chain brake
- It is essential that the chain brake is operative at all times.
- Chain brake must be checked before using the saw (refer to daily maintenance).
- By frequent operation of the brake throughout the day, the brake's internal components are kept free from an accumulation of dirt and saw dust.
- Frequent lubrication of the pivot or sliding surfaces is necessary to ensure effective operation.
- For chain brake adjustment, refer to a competent chainsaw mechanic.

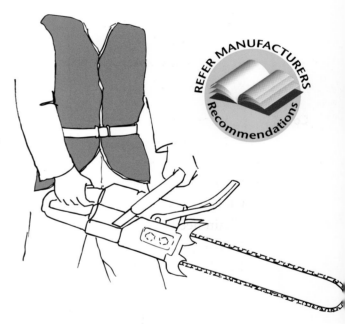

REFER MANUFACTURERS Recommendations

Oil system
- Check operation, clean as necessary.

Cooling fans
- Remove fan housing, clean fan and cylinder fins.

Rubber mountings
- Check for looseness and deterioration.

Sprocket/clutch
- Remove, clean debris from clutch and sprocket.
- Check sprocket for wear. Replace if necessary (must also renew chain).
- Grease bearing.

Spark arrester
- When engine performance begins to deteriorate, remove and clean spark arrester. The spark arrester must be securely fitted at all times.

Tune engine (with a tachometer)
- Adjust low speed jet.
- Adjust high speed jet.
- Adjust idle.

Grease sprocket nose.

- Clean lubricating hole – where fitted.
- Grease nose on each refill - where fitted.

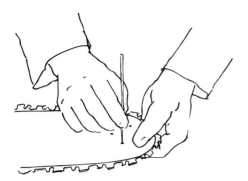
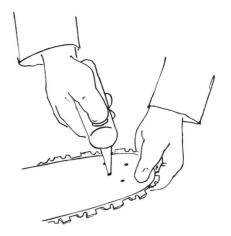

Guide bar maintenance

The groove should be kept clean and the clearance to the bottom of the chain drive links maintained at 1.0 mm

- Remove burred or feathered edges with a flat file
- Check the oil holes regularly to ensure they are clear
- Turn bar regularly to ensure even wear
- Ensure chain entry point is properly funnelled
- Ensure the rails are even and run at right angles to the body of the bar.

REFER MANUFACTURERS Recommendations

Common features of chain

Any chain problem is caused by one or more of the following:

- Chain needs to be sharpened correctly
- Chain needs lubricating
- Chain needs to be tensioned correctly
- Depth gauges need to be set correctly.

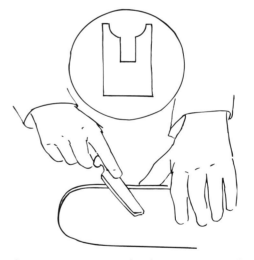

Important: Both the gauge of the chainsaw and the grove width of the guide bar must match

Engine tuning

Satisfactory engine tuning can only be achieved if all parts of the power head are functioning properly, i.e.:

- Air flow – clean air filter
- Fuel flow – clean tank
- Fuel filter
- Correct petrol/oil mix
- Electrical current – correctly gapped and clean spark plug.

Chainsaw power head trouble-shooting chart

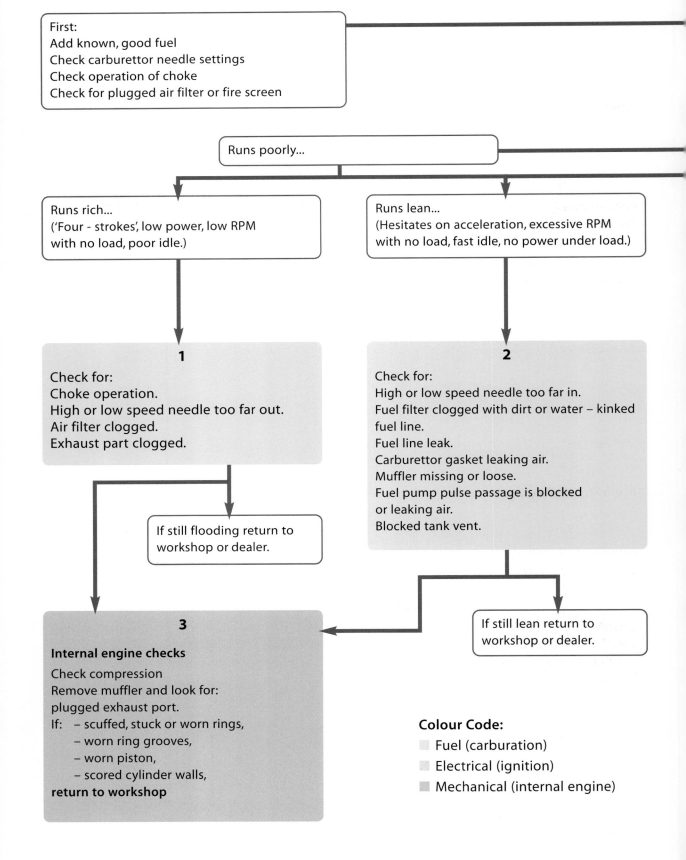

First:
Add known, good fuel
Check carburettor needle settings
Check operation of choke
Check for plugged air filter or fire screen

Runs poorly...

Runs rich...
('Four - strokes', low power, low RPM with no load, poor idle.)

Runs lean...
(Hesitates on acceleration, excessive RPM with no load, fast idle, no power under load.)

1
Check for:
Choke operation.
High or low speed needle too far out.
Air filter clogged.
Exhaust part clogged.

2
Check for:
High or low speed needle too far in.
Fuel filter clogged with dirt or water – kinked fuel line.
Fuel line leak.
Carburettor gasket leaking air.
Muffler missing or loose.
Fuel pump pulse passage is blocked or leaking air.
Blocked tank vent.

If still flooding return to workshop or dealer.

If still lean return to workshop or dealer.

3

Internal engine checks

Check compression
Remove muffler and look for:
plugged exhaust port.
If: – scuffed, stuck or worn rings,
      – worn ring grooves,
      – worn piston,
      – scored cylinder walls,
return to workshop

Colour Code:
Fuel (carburation)
Electrical (ignition)
Mechanical (internal engine)

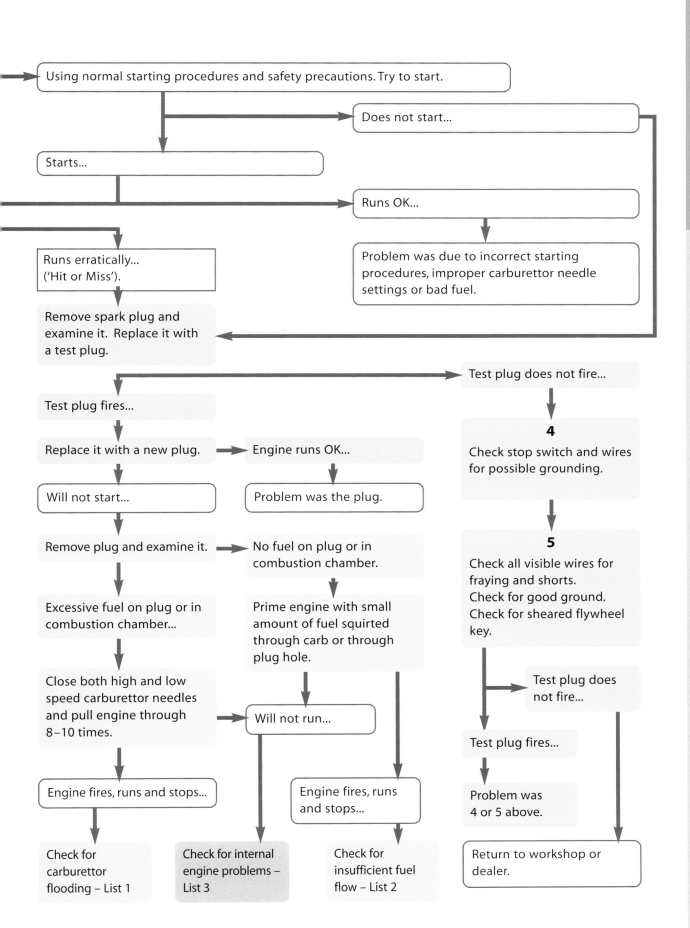

The cutting attachment

The cutting attachment on a chainsaw does the real work when the saw is operating. Therefore it is essential that all three components, sprocket/guide bar/chain are properly maintained for the saw to be used efficiently and safely.

The sprocket/guide bar/chain, work as a closely related trio. If any of these parts are not in top working order, problems will result in the other two, e.g. a loose chain will cause rapid wear behind the nose of the bar and will increase wear on the guide bar.

Sprockets

The clutch transmits power through the clutch drum to the sprocket. The sprocket pulls the chain around the bar and through the wood.

The sprocket is a gear, and gear terminology is used to name its parts.

Sprocket types:

• Spur (fixed)
• Rim (floating)

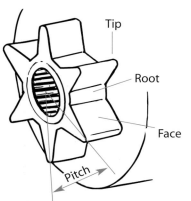
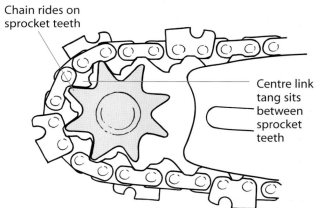

Spur sprockets

Spur sprockets have wide tooth faces which engage the chain's drive link tangs. These wide faces help in the alignment of the chain to the guide bar groove. The spur sprocket supports the chain either on the tip of the teeth or by nesting the drive link tang between the sprocket teeth.

Spur sprockets are permanently attached to the clutch drum. They have the advantages of good bark and chip removal but tend to be hard on the chain.

Rim sprockets

Rim type sprockets look like a wheel because they have the sprocket teeth mounted between two rims. The rims support the tie straps and cutters thus allowing the chain to run more smoothly with less wear. The drive link (tangs) of the chain are engaged by the faces of the sprocket teeth. Chip removal is by way of discharge holes on the side of the rim.

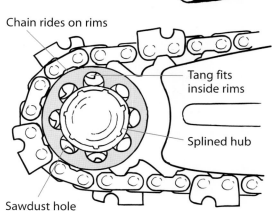

Rim sprocket

Discharge holes face away from clutch drum

The rim sprocket is mounted on a splined hub, welded to the clutch drum. This spline allows the rim sprocket to self align with the guide bar groove.

The more common type of rim is now the Radial Port Rim. This sprocket uses a system of radial ports to discharge the wood chips.

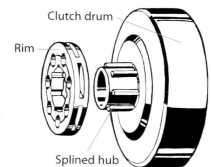

Sprocket replacement

Drive sprockets are subjected to extreme heat and friction and therefore wear. A worn sprocket will damage and weaken a chain beyond repair, cause a loss of cutting power and accelerate guide bar wear.

Manufacturers recommend installing a new sprocket with each new chain fitted. However, sprocket life can be extended by using 2 chains per sprocket with chains being alternated daily.

To avoid sprocket problems

- Replace when worn with a correctly pitched sprocket.
- Each new sprocket = 2 new chains.
- Keep chain well sharpened.
- Keep chain correctly tensioned.
- Grease bearing each fortnight or upon sprocket removal from saw.
- Keep guide bar rails in good order.
- Maintain a good oil flow in guide bar groove.

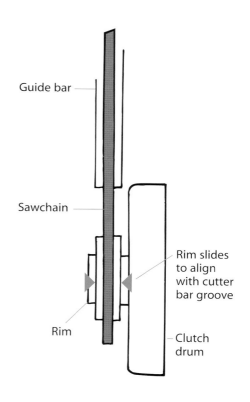

Sprocket pitch

It is important that chain and sprocket pitch are matched.

The pitch of the chain is determined by measuring from the distance between 3 adjacent rivets divided by 2.

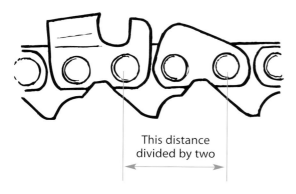

This distance divided by two

Chain pitch

Level 1

The cutting attachment

Guide bar

Guide bar types:

- Solid nose
- Laminated sprocket nose
- Guide bar with replaceable sprocket nose

Solid nose bar

As most of the friction between guide bar and chain is generated at the tip of the bar and most wear occurs there, the solid nose bar has a layer of hard-wearing stellate around the nose of the bar.

Solid nose profiles:

- wide
- narrow

Cross section

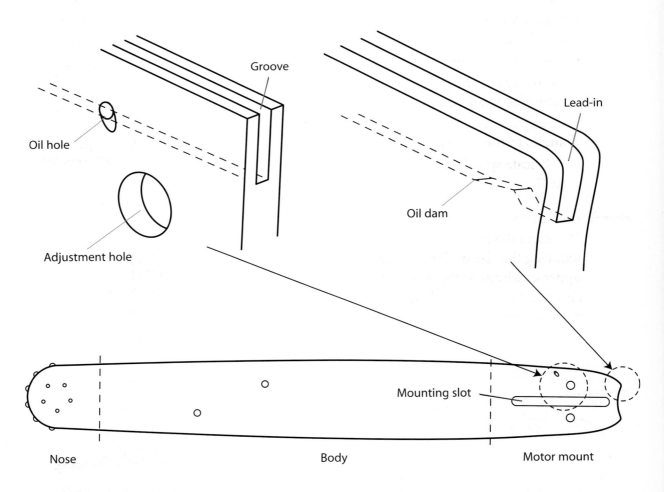

Sprocket nose guide bar

Sprocket nose bar

A sprocket nose guide bar allows the sawchain to run more tightly than a solid nose bar. The sprocket reduces friction, thus allowing more power to be delivered to the sawchain.

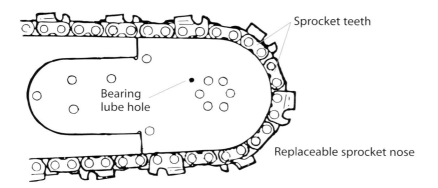

Sprocket teeth

Bearing lube hole

Replaceable sprocket nose

Guide bar maintenance

- Keep the groove clean and maintain the clearance to the bottom of the chain drive links at 1 mm (1/32 in).
- Remove feathered or burred edges with a flat file or stone.
- Check the oil holes regularly to ensure they are clean.
- Turn guide bar daily to ensure even wear.
- Ensure chain entry point is properly funnelled (lead-in).
- Ensure the rails are even and run at right angles to the body of the guide bar.
- Lubricate sprocket bar tip with each tank refill.

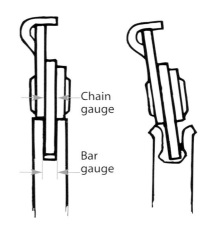

Chain gauge

Bar gauge

Bar gauge helps support chain

Bar gauge too wide, chain leans over

Narrow profile sprocket nose bar

Decreases the risk of kick-back by reducing the size of danger area in the upper quadrant of the nose. There are also less cutters in the danger area at any one time.

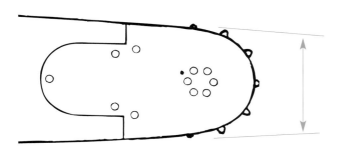

Narrower than full profile sprocket nose guide bar

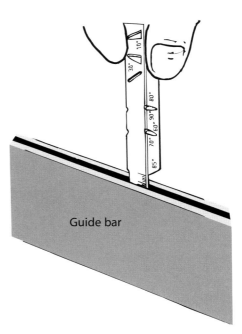

Guide bar

Special tool used to clean out guide bar groove

Sawchain

Chains are made in many different types, shapes and sizes, but all chains have common features:

- They need to be sharpened correctly
- They need lubricating
- They need to be tensioned correctly
- Their depth gauges need to be set correctly

Chain components:

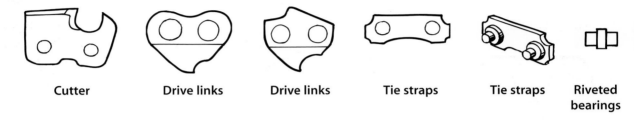

| Cutter | Drive links | Drive links | Tie straps | Tie straps | Riveted bearings |

Cutters

Sawchain has both left and right cutters. Each cutter has a top plate and side plate which are sharpened to a fine edge and regularly need to be re-sharpened to keep the chain operating at top performance.

The top plate feeds the cutter into the wood and the side plate severs the side of the cutting track.

The working corner (intersection of top and side plates) severs the cross grain.

To control the amount of wood taken at one bite each cutter has a finger-like projection at the front called a depth gauge.

The base of each cutter has three areas: the toe, the heel and the notch. The toe at the front and the heel at the rear slide on the guide bar. The notch provides clearance to allow the centre link to rest between the teeth and a spur sprocket.

The toe at the front and the heel at the rear slide on the rails.

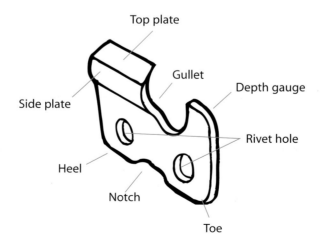

Drive links

The tang is the part of the drive link on which the sprocket drives the chain. The hook of the tang picks up oil and carries it along the bar for lubrication. The hook also forms a scraper which keeps the bar groove clean. The tang, by riding in the bar groove keeps the chain aligned on the bar.

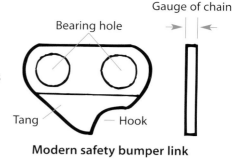

Modern safety bumper link

Tie straps

The tie strap is the connecting link between the cutter and the drive links as well as a spacing link between the cutters.

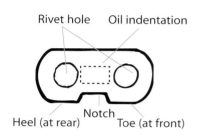

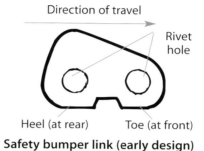

Safety bumper link (early design)

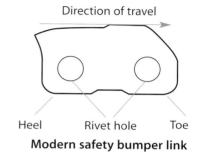

Modern safety bumper link

Set

The amount of set decreases as the cutter top plate is worn backwards and the side plate slopes inwards towards the rear of the cutter.

This is the reason why some well worn chains will not successfully cut thick heavy bark, i.e. reduced amount of off-set.

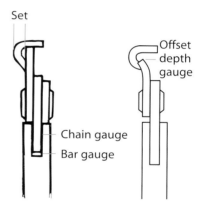

Kerf

This is the width of the cut made into the wood by the chain.

Gauge

This is the thickness of the tang of the drive link.

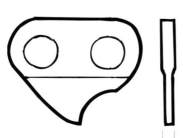

Thickness of bottom section of drive link (0.043– .050– .058– .063)

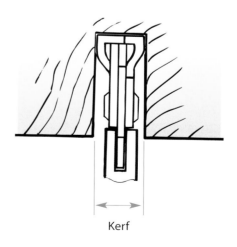

Cutter types

Round or chipper profile

Slow cutting but stays sharper longer due to large cutting corner.

Square or chisel profile

Fast cutting but has fine cutting corner, easily blunted in abrasive cutting.

Semi-square or semi-chisel

Compromise between round and square profiles.

Chamfer chisel

Narrow-kerf chain that requires less power to cut the wood.
Similar to the cutting action of semi-square chain.

| Round profile | Square profile | Semi-square profile | Camfer chisel profile |

Common filing angles

	Round	Semi-square	Square
Top plate filing angle	30°	30°*	25°
Side plate filing angle	90°	85°	90°
File tilt	nil	nil	nil

* with semi-square profile chains, the top plate is filed at 35° but because of slight tilt (up to 5° tilt), a 30° angle should be obtained.

Reduced vibration chain

Not to be confused with sawchain which is designed to reduce the tendency of kick-back.

Some sawchain manufactures market a sawchain which is designed to reduce the vibration inherit in the cutting process of sawchain. This particular design is available to a number of sawchain types.

Note: Chainsaw and sawchain manufacturers are continually upgrading their products. Seek guidance from your local chainsaw retailer as to the most appropriate chain type that best suits your particular needs or situation.

Sawchain sharpening

The chain should be sharpened when:
- The chainsaw requires undue force to make it cut.
- Saw dust consists of fine powder.
- Chainsaw starts to dish or run off in the cut.
- If damage is present on the chrome surface of top plate or side plate.

Always use the correct diameter file for the particular chain.
File diameter is governed by the chain's pitch.

Sawchain sharpening – Round file diameter

Chain pitch	File diameter (round file)
1/4″	5/32″ (4 mm)
0.325″	5/32″ to 3/16″ (4.5 mm)
3/8″ Low Profile	5/32″ (4 mm)
3/8″ Standard	13/64″ to 7/32″ (5.5 mm)
0.404″	7/32″ to 1/4″ (5.5 mm to 6 mm)

Generally the larger diameter file is used until the cutter is half worn, then smaller diameter file is used. Points to remember when filing:
- File using a full length stroke.
- The art of sharpening is to 'hone' rather than the removal of a lot of metal.
- Don't attempt to sharpen an oily chain.
- Cut some dry wood to clear oil from chain.
- File a little bit often, rather than a lot occasionally.
- Cutters should be filed from inside to outside.
- Keep cutters equal in length and angles. Failure to do so will cause uneven cutting (running off) chain chatter and excessive vibration.
- When using a file guide, ensure that the guide rests both on the top plate and depth gauge.
- Sharpen with saw firmly positioned.
- Match file diameter to file guide.
- File until all damage is removed from top plate and side plate, i.e. back to chrome surface.

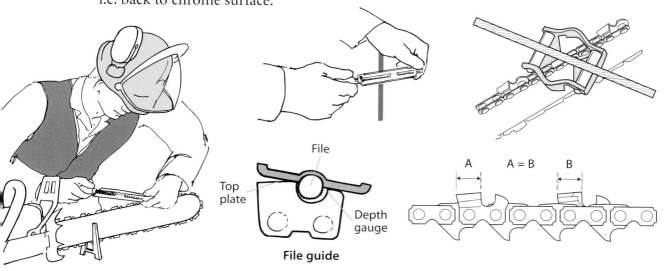

Top plate

File

Depth gauge

File guide

A   A = B   B

Depth gauge setting

Depth gauge setting is critical to the performance of the chain.

Depth gauge too low	Chain grabs, binds easily, chatters and leads to rapid cutter bar wear.
Depth gauge too high	Chain loses self feeding characteristics and extra pressure is required to get the chain to cut. Leads to rapid wear on all components.
Uneven depth gauge setting	Gives excessive vibration and chain chatter.

Check depth gauges every 3rd or 4th sharpen. In order to maintain maximum performance throughout the entire life of the chain, the depth gauges must be lowered progressively as the cutter's length is reduced.

The potential for kick-back is reduced by rounding the front of the depth gauge.

Depth gauge setting varies depending on chain type, saw power and wood to be cut.

0.025″	pine small saws
0.0250″ to 0.030″	general cutting hardwood large saws

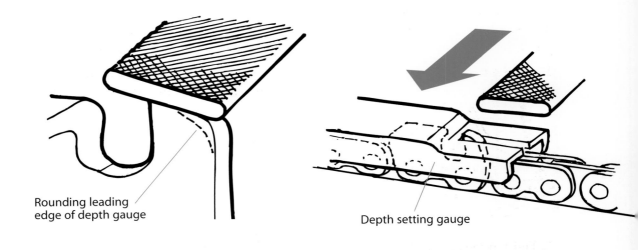

Rounding leading edge of depth gauge

Depth setting gauge

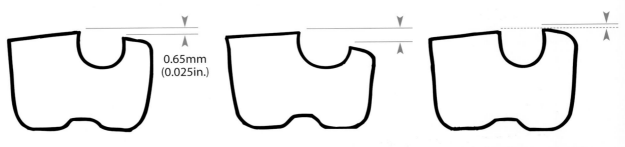

0.65mm
(0.025in.)

**Correct depth gauge setting
0.025″ to 0.035″**

Low depth gauge setting

High depth gauge setting

'Breaking in' a new sawchain

It is important to take care to progressively 'break in' a new chain to ensure it is thoroughly lubricated.

Procedure

1. Tension new chain normally.

2. Pour oil onto chain and guide bar

3. Run chain at 1/2 throttle for 1 to 2 minutes (no load).

4. Stop saw and allow to cool – re-tension if necessary.

5. Cut for 2 to 3 minutes at 1/2 throttle.

6. Stop saw and allow to cool – re-tension if necessary.

7. Chain is now ready for use.

Note: Never re-tension a very hot chain and leave overnight. Contraction could bend the crankshaft.

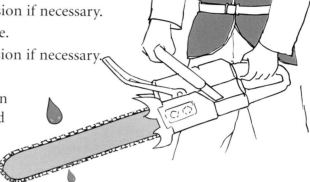

Thoroughly lubricate a new chain before use

Chain tension

Correct chain tension is where the bottom of the chains tie straps are just touching the underside of the guide bar.

1. Loosen bar nuts.

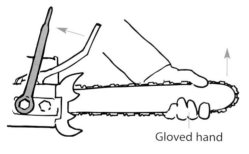
Gloved hand

2. Tighten tension screw. Tighten until chain just touches bottom bar rails. Chain on sprocket nose bars should be tighter.

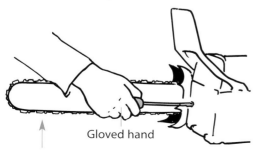
Gloved hand

Chain must be able to be pulled around the bar freely by hand. Sprocket nose bars require chain to be tensioned slightly tighter

3. Pull chain around bar to be sure it fits sprocket and bar.

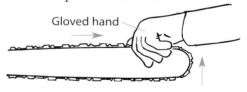
Gloved hand

4. Hold bar tip up. Tighten nuts.

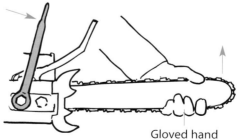
Gloved hand

Sawchain tension

Hand filing

Round chipper and microbit

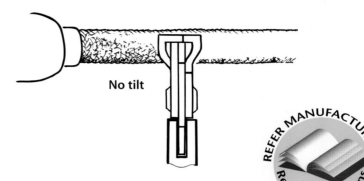

No tilt

REFER MANUFACTURERS Recommendations

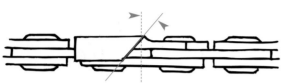

Top plate angle 25° to 30°

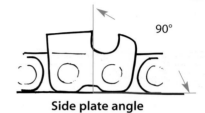

90°

Side plate angle

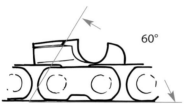

60°

Top plate cutting angle

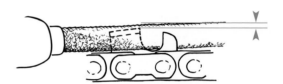

1/10 of the file diameter above cutter top plate

Semi-square micro chisel

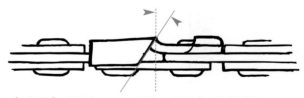

Top plate angle 30° for 3/8" gauge, 30° to 35° for 0.404" gauge.

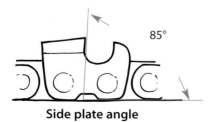

85°

Side plate angle

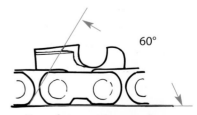

60°

Top plate cutting angle

Square chisel

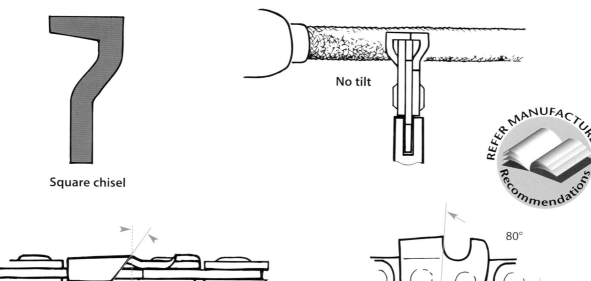

Square chisel

No tilt

REFER MANUFACTURERS
Recommendations

Top plate angle 25° to 30°

80°

Side plate angle

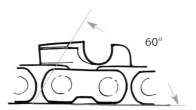

60°

Top plate cutting angle 60°

Square chisel (low profile)

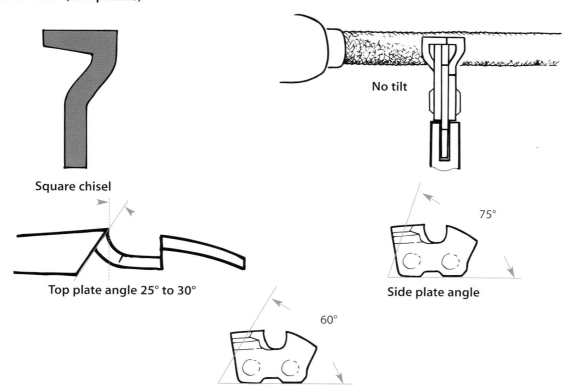

Square chisel

No tilt

Top plate angle 25° to 30°

75°

Side plate angle

60°

Top plate cutting angle 60°

Chamfer chisel

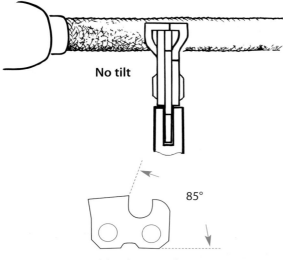

No tilt

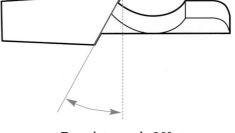

Top plate angle 30°

85°

Side plate angle 85°

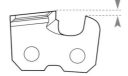

60°

Top plate angle 60°

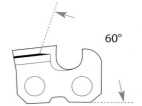

Square-ground chain

Filing

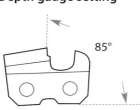

Depth gauge setting

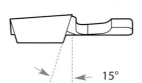

15°

Top plate angle

85°

Side plate angle

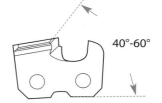

40°-60°

Top plate cutting angle

File positioning

The file will sharpen the top plate, the side plate, simultaneously. This creates a line (A), where the top plate cutting angle meets the side plate angle. For best results, file so that the line joins the cutting corner (B).

Correctly filed corner

Incorrectly filed corner

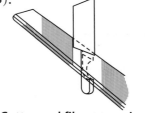

Cutter and file at top view

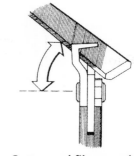

Cutter and file at end view

Filing direction

It is recommended that square-ground chain be filed from outside in, in a downward direction. This leaves a better edge on the chromed cutting surfaces and makes it easier to keep the file's position, and the resulting cutting edges, in correct alignment. Accurate positioning of the file during filing is important. File all cutters on one side of the chain, then reverse the chain and repeat the process. Use the same file positions for cutters on the opposite side of the chain.

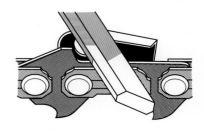

Downward filing direction

Sawchain design

Over the past two decades, there has been worldwide research to find answers to the problem of kick-back.

In the early 1980s chain makers designed a ramp into the tie strap between the cutters. The purpose of the ramp was to ease the cutter's depth gauge over the obstacle. This design was the 1st generation safety chain.

The design was further developed to include a ramp in the drive link and then the depth gauge. Modern sawchain is designed with any of the above features.

Today, chain manufactures market a range of sawchain designed to satisfy particular functions e.g. low vibration, anti-kick-back, ability to resist abrasion, specialised applications e.g. heavy bark, ripping.

It is the responsibility of the chainsaw user to identify the particular chain that best suits their particular application and working conditions.

Note: Chainsaw and sawchain manufacturers are continually upgrading their product. Several different designs of chain profiles have come onto the market in recent years. Seek the guidance of your local chainsaw retailer regarding the most suitable chain type to suit your requirements.

Basic 'anti-kick-back' chain types

A chain is made up of a number of links, which are available in standard and low kick-back versions

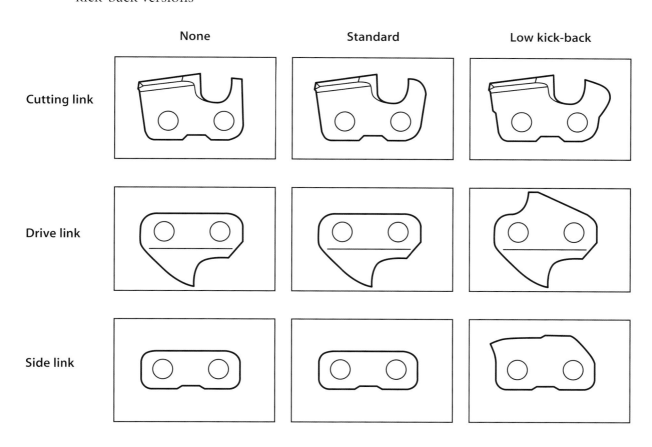

Combining these links in different ways gives different degrees of kick-back reduction. In terms of kick-back reduction alone, four different types of link are available.

Level 1 — Sawchain design

Kick-back situations

Standard chain (non-safety)

Timber strikes vertical face of depth gauge

Sawchain without any kick-back protection is not recommended

Early 'reduced kick-back' chain (1st generation)

The ramp on the tie strap guides the obstacle onto the cutter.

Modern sawchain with reduced kick-back

The cutter's depth gauge has the ramp built in, thus smoothly guiding the cutter into the timber.

This sawchain is used by professional chainsaw operators. Do not use this type of sawchain unless you have received specialised training for dealing with kick-back.

Modern low kick-back chain

This type of chain offers the most effective kick-back protection.

Recommended for all kinds of chainsaw operation including the occasional operator.

Technical information regarding the cutting attachment and sawchain maintenance is courtesy of Husqvarna and Oregon.

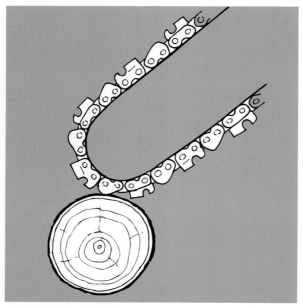

Reduced kick-back chain

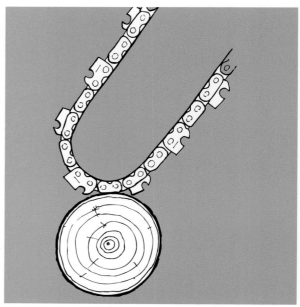

Non-safety chain

40 | Chainsaw Operator's Manual

Cross-cutting sequence

The importance of good cross-cutting techniques are to:

- Minimise the chance of injury.
- Minimise damage to powerhead and cutting attachment.
- Minimise jamming of saw.
- Maximise utilisation of felled timber.

Basic principles of cross-cutting

- Always assess the bind relationships (internal tension in timber) in the log and choose sequence of cuts to suit.
- Stand to one side of cut.
- If there is a chance of either half of the log springing, keep an escape route open.
- Stand on the opposite side to which a log will spring or roll (stand on the uphill side of log if it is likely to roll).
- Wherever possible cut the opposite side of the log first. This will keep the operator as far away from the log as possible, when the release cut is made. This will minimise the chance of saw jamming.
- To minimise up-cutting (it's hard work), boring in and down cutting may be easier.
- Watch kerf to see whether it is opening or closing. May cause you to alter sequence of cuts.
- If there is a risk of log pinching or jamming the guide bar, 'saw' back and forth during the cut. This makes it easier to feel when the log is beginning to pinch the guide bar.
- 'Sawing' the chainsaw back and forth is effective when cutting badly split timber – widens the kerf of the cut.
- Use the saw as a lever and the logs as a pivot point to minimise work effort. Similarly use the leg muscles when cutting upwards.
- Insert a wedge in the cut if there is a high risk of the log dropping or twisting. This will prevent jamming.

Always stand on the uphill side of the log

Assessment of internal stress in fallen timber

In cross-cutting, always cut the wood in compression first, be it on the top, bottom or on either side. If wood in compression is cut last, then saw will jam or timber will split horizontally.

Types of binds

Top bind

Both ends supported.

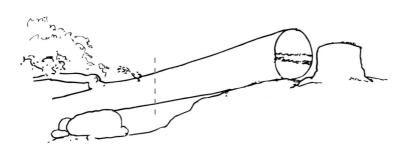

Small log

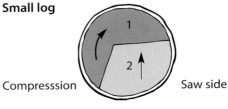

Compresssion   Saw side

Large log

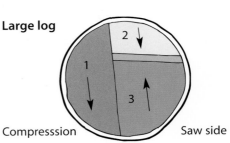

Compresssion   Saw side

Top bind using a wedge

Note: Technique is to cut timber in one downward action, putting in wedge when clear of guide bar.

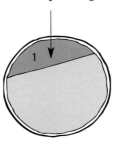      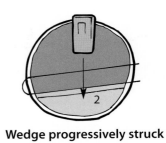

Wedge in place   Wedge progressively struck

Not to be used on large timber

Bottom bind

One end supported

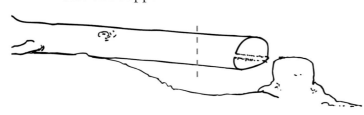

Small log

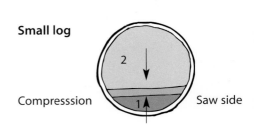

Compresssion   Saw side

Large log

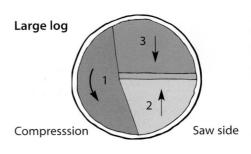

Compresssion   Saw side

Side blind

Where a log lies across the slope with a side unable to move because of stumps or other logs, side bind can occur. Work from the compression side.

Cut a small 'v' piece (scarf) from compression side of log.

This will allow pressure to be released gradually and may release all pressure before final (release) cut is completed.

Care must be taken to ensure 'v' cut is not too deep, as the saw may jam.

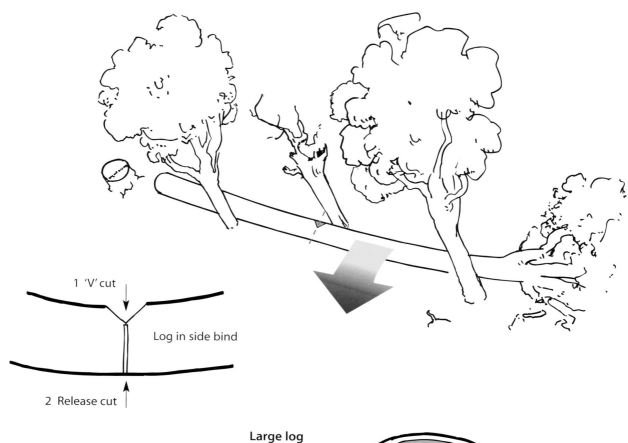

1 'V' cut

Log in side bind

2 Release cut

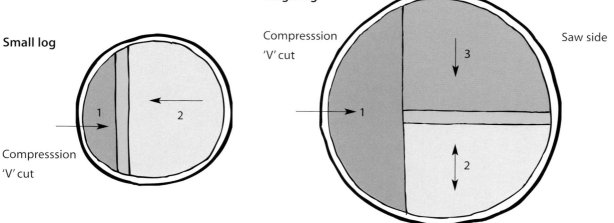

Small log

1

2

Compresssion 'V' cut

Large log

Compresssion 'V' cut

Saw side

3

1

2

Note:

1. It may be very dangerous to attempt to cross-cut a large diameter tree that is lying under significant side bind tension. Side bind tension should be progressively released by removing the tree's head before attempting the required cut.

2. When putting in the final cut, operator should stand on the opposite side of the expected motion of the timber.

Log trap

Before beginning the cuts through a log check for any possible lateral movement. If one end of the log is unable to move and the other end can drop away when cut, an angled cut is used.

Ensure that the angle cut is sloped to the correct side so that the release cut will not cause the cutter bar to be trapped when one end drops away.

Sequence of cuts

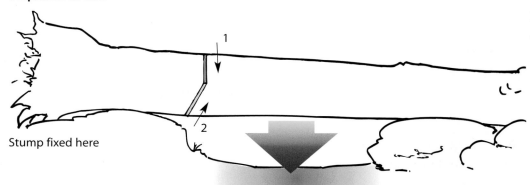

Stump fixed here

Alternative method

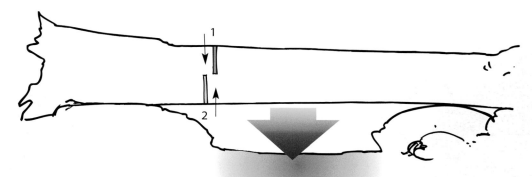

Removing trees that have fallen across a road

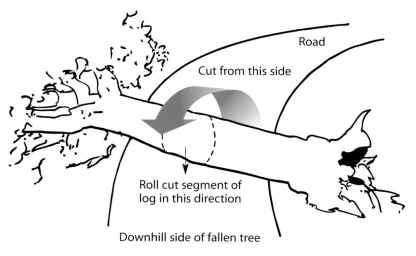

Road

Cut from this side

Roll cut segment of log in this direction

Downhill side of fallen tree

Wind blow

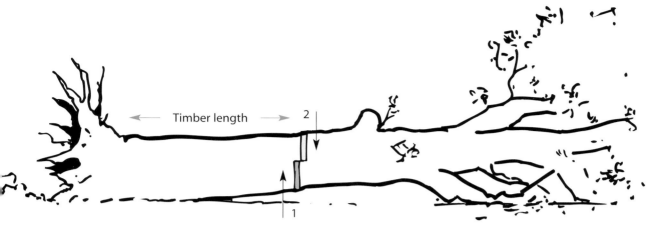

Timber length

Tree with partially buried or obstructed stump

Note: Staggered cut should be placed on the portion of the tree that will not move upon completion of release cut. This avoids both the saw jamming and saw being flung away as the root ball returns to its original position.

Stagger final cut away from the stump to avoid jamming the saw

Limbing

When limbing caution is the word. Always be aware of where the nose of the guide bar is at all times. There is a real danger of the operator being injured by branches swinging back or dropping down or the tree shifting during the limbing process.

General basic rules:

- Stand in a safe working position and watch out for obstacles.
- Where possible never limb on the side of the tree you are standing.
- Concentrate on what you are doing.
- Always be aware where the nose of the guide bar is.

- Limb should be cut off about 50 cm from trunk and then flush trimmed if necessary.

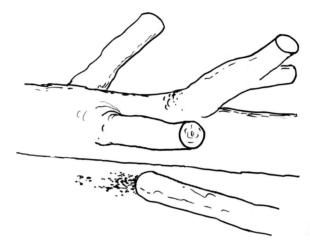

- At times it may be necessary to work the saw horizontally. Adjust your grip on the chainsaw's handles to suit the position of the saw.

- Whenever possible, let the tree support the weight of the chainsaw. Pivot the saw, using the saw's dogs (spikes) as a fulcrum. Where this is not possible, support the weight of the saw with your thigh.

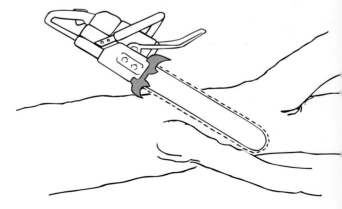

Limbing small to medium-sized conifers (softwood)

The relative regular distribution of branches on conifer trees should permit a systematic work pattern following the whorls (rings) of branches. This work pattern can be used to effectively limb the tree.

The operator stands on the left side of the tree. Operator works from the butt to the top of the tree. The saw moves from the right to the left on the first ring (1) (2) (3), and then moves to the next ring, this time cutting from left to right (4) (5) (6).

This technique requires that the operator does part of the limbing with a forward-running chain (1) (2) (4) (5), and the remainder with a backward-running chain (3) (6).

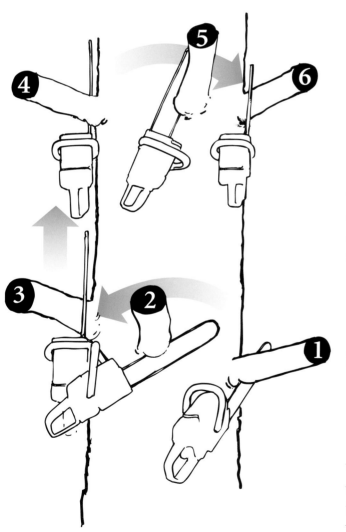

When the tree lies in a hollow, the branches on the underside of the two rings are cut in one movement before the operator moves forward to the next two rings.

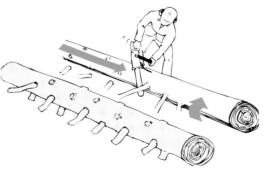

When the tree lies on the ground it is turned when the operator has worked his/her way to the top. The remaining branches are cut while the operator returns to the butt of the tree.

Limbing large trees e.g. eucalyptus (hardwoods)

This operation requires much attention to avoid:

- kick-back
- the guide bar becoming pinched
- the wood cracking
- the operator being injured by branches swinging back or dropping down, or by the tree shifting.

The following rules should be observed:

1. First cut and remove branches hindering your work.
   - cut branches in two or more sections when there is a danger of cracking at the base or when this facilitates clearing work area (a) (b) (c).
   - keep your working space clear of cut branches.
2. It is very important to observe the tensions in the wood, particularly on large branches.

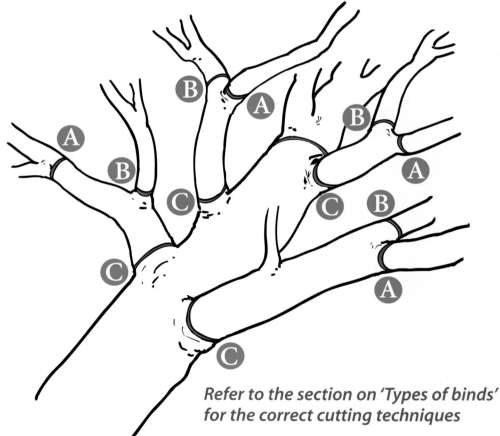

Refer to the section on 'Types of binds' for the correct cutting techniques

Step cut

When limbing large limbs it may be necessary to incorporate a step cut.

- Step is located on stationary portion of limb.
- Chainsaw will not fall down with moving limb.

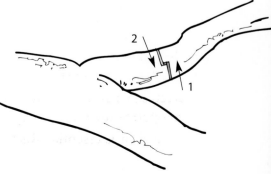

Butt trimming

Butt trimming or pre-limbing trees may be necessary in order to remove branches that may get in the way during the felling operation. (Particularly important in softwood felling.)

Butt trimming is very dangerous due to high risk of kick-back

Basic principles:

- Don't cut branches above shoulder height. Saw will have a strong tendency to kick-back and physical control is poor.
- Hold so that guide bar is at right angles to your body; in this way, if the saw does kick-back there is little risk of it striking you. (Keep out of the kick-back line during any chainsaw operation where kick-back risk is high.)
- Work around tree in an anti-clockwise direction.
- Keep saw parallel to your shoulders. Arms and wrist straight. (It may be necessary to operate the throttle trigger with your thumb in this position.)
- Face visor is essential. Risk of eye injury is high due to flying chips.

Level 2
Simple tree felling

(Intermediate competence of safe chainsaw operation – harvest trees manually)

Theory of felling

Features of a competent faller:

- Planning
- Steady pace
- Concentration
- Low risk technique

A 'competent' faller is one who controls the situation, and never lets it control themselves by working outside the limits of their own abilities.

When assessing a tree to determine the desired direction of fall, consider:

- Natural lean of the tree
- Weight distribution of crown
- Intergrowth with adjoining trees
- Wind
- Hung-ups
- Climbing vines
- Open space
- Special conditions

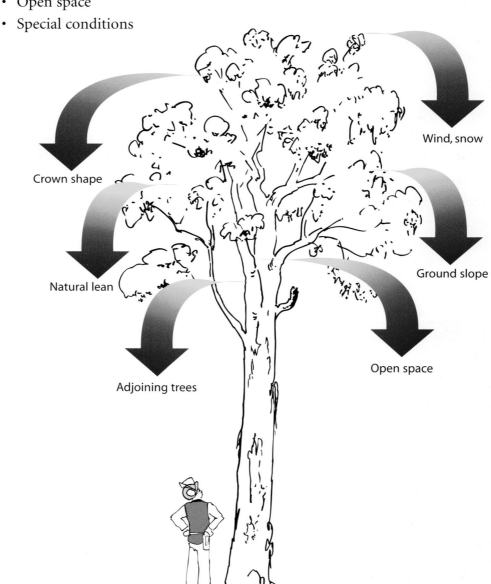

Crown shape

Wind, snow

Natural lean

Ground slope

Adjoining trees

Open space

Importance of directional felling

A competent faller aims to fell the tree in the desired direction of fall, without injury to themselves or other people, damage to equipment, sound timber on ground, retrained trees, or the tree being felled.

Therefore directional felling is important for:

- Own safety
- Safety of others
  - don't leave 'hangers' or 'widow makers'
- Work pattern
  - ease of extraction by machinery
  - covering up other felled trees
- Recovery (utilisation)
  - shattering logs
  - smashing regeneration

Considerations before felling each tree

(Assessment of a standing tree)

Natural lean of tree

It is difficult to fell a tree against all but a moderate lean.

An axe, used as a 'plumb bob', can be used to judge the tree's natural lean.

Which tree to fell next

Operator needs to consider sequence of felling trees to guard against:

- creating hangers or widow makers
- creating hang-ups
- creating extra work through placing heads of trees or limbs at the base of another tree to be felled.

Weight distribution of crown

Determine which side of crown has the most weight.

Branching or heavy growth on one side will tend to drag the tree in that direction.

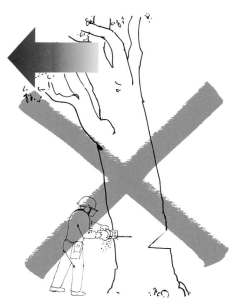

Check the lean

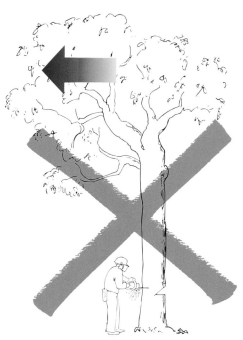

Check the weight distribution

Check for defect
- Sound tree with axe.
- Look for external scars, deadwoods in crown, burnt sections, ants, etc.
- May have to adjust felling direction.
- Some species of trees are prone to defects in heart, e.g. pipes.
- Internal defects can be detected by the condition of the saw dust.

Intergrowth with adjoining trees
Trees may be difficult to fell when:
- intergrown with adjacent trees.
- vines interwoven with adjacent trees.

Avoid felling trees that brush against other trees. These may result in:
- falling limbs.
- making widow makers.
- possible hangers.

Never work underneath lodged or hung-up trees

Open spaces
- Always fell into open space (even small trees in the felling line can be thrown back towards stump).
- Create own open space by working on felling face whenever possible.
- Avoid felling into other trees, stumps, rocks or logs if possible.

Wind
- May be strong enough to overcome the tree's natural lean or crown out of balance.
- May have to wait for 'lull' in wind under gusting conditions before felling.
- Wind velocity always less at ground level than crown level. (Wind acts on the tree head in similar manner to wind acting on a sail of a sailing boat.)
- Avoid using chainsaws in wet or windy conditions.

Hangers or widow makers
Take extra care when felling a tree with a hanger in it. First stage of a tree's fall may dislodge the hanger – continue watching during escape.

Hung-up trees
Trees that have lodged together after felling must be immediately and completely felled or otherwise made safe to persons who may pass underneath.

All hung-up trees must be marked with a suitable sign displaying 'Danger Hang-Up'.

Refer to felling hung-up trees.

Special conditions
Include the presence of fences, power lines, filter strips, etc.

Preparation at each tree prior to felling

Clean around base of tree

- Prepare a clean work area around tree.
- Remove small bushes to enable a good footing and to prevent 'kick-back' through guide bar striking hidden obstacle.
- Clean dead wood, etc. along tree felling line. May be flung up/backwards, upon tree's impact.
- Clear around base of tree
- Prepare an escape route

Be sure of your footing

Prepare escape route

The majority of felling accidents occur within 4 metres of the stump.

- Choose a line of retreat 45° diagonally backwards, away from the direction of fall.
- If the butt kicks up as the tree falls, it will generally go straight backwards or to one side.
- If tree splits up it will slab backwards from the line of fall.
- If tree snaps in falling line it will generally come back straight over stump.
- When felling trees uphill, they may slide straight backwards over the stump.

> *Caution: This is a dangerous practice, and if it must be done, should be carried out by a competent chainsaw operator.*

- When tree begins to fall (i.e. when fibres in holding wood begin to snap)
  – withdraw saw
  – withdraw along intended escape route
  – continuously look back at tree's fall, check for flying/falling limbs
  – do not re-enter felling site until all movement has ceased

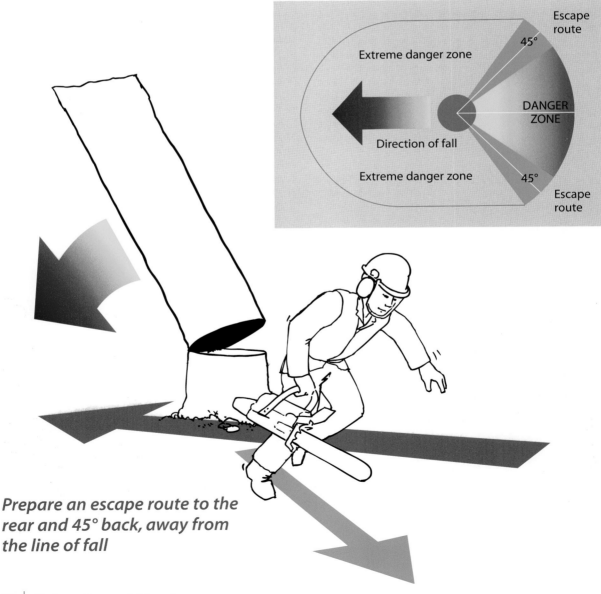

Prepare an escape route to the rear and 45° back, away from the line of fall

Don't cut above shoulder height

Always ensure you have a comfortable working position standing on firm ground.

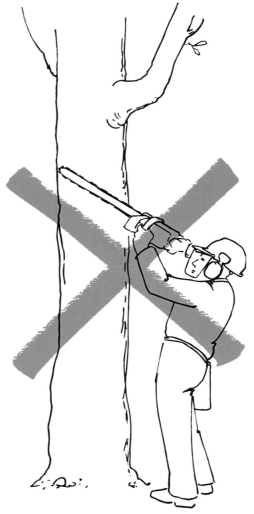

Don't attempt to cut above shoulder height

Think before you act

Think safe and plan ahead

Theory of simple tree felling

Scarf

Function of scarf
- Directs tree in desired direction of fall
- Controls tree during fall (Allows smooth steady fall of tree)
- Serves as a means of breaking holding wood
- Helps to prevent tree from splitting up.

Types of scarf are:
- Standard 45° Pine, 30° Hardwood
- Humbolt or reverse scarf
- V scarf
- Box scarf
- 90° scarf

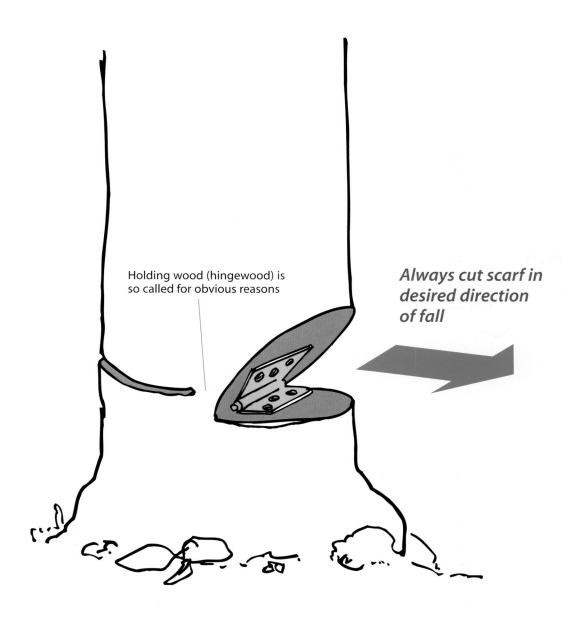

Holding wood (hingewood) is
so called for obvious reasons

*Always cut scarf in
desired direction
of fall*

Standard scarf

- Most common used.
- Consists of horizontal and angled open cuts.
- Both cuts are to finish at the same depth in the tree.
- Scarf wood should be able to be removed cleanly.

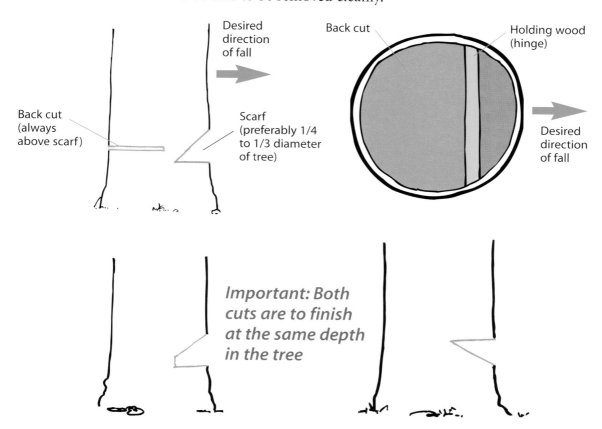

Important: Both cuts are to finish at the same depth in the tree

Features of a scarf

Direction
– must be in direction of desired fall

Depth
– 1/4 to 1/3 diameter of tree

Size of Opening
– 45° Softwood, 30° Hardwood

Cuts
– both cuts must intersect at a given point

Intersection points
– line between both intersection points should be approximately horizontal

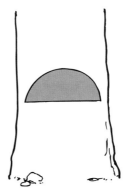

Technique for cutting the scarf

Aim along the desired direction of fall.

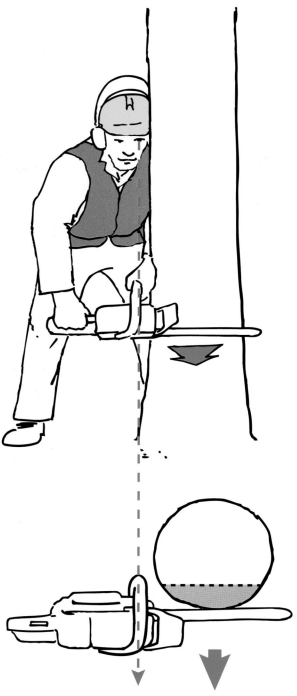

Desired direction of fall

B. Support your body and right knee against the tree to relieve the strain on your back and enable you the guide the saw better.

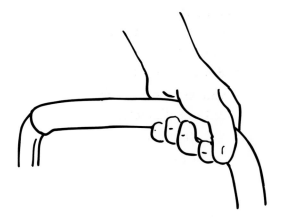

A. Align 'gunning sight' along the desired direction of fall.

On some saws, the front handle can be used to align the felling direction.

C. Grip the top edge of the front handle, since this will tilt the saw at the right angle for sawing the upper cut.

Other types of scarf

Humbolt scarf

- Frequently used in saw log operation.
- Sometimes difficult to cut very low to the ground.
- Can be an advantage when felling uphill. This cut provides an extra 'step' to prevent the tree sliding back over stump.

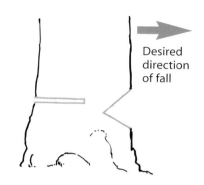

Desired direction of fall

*V scarf

- Fairly difficult – must match the two sloping cuts.
- Advantage in that this scarf gives a very wide mouth opening. Tree falls under control through greater angle.
- Can be used to advantage when felling trees with trunk diameters larger than twice the chainsaw's cutter bar length.

  (See section on 'Tree with diameter twice cutter bar length'.)

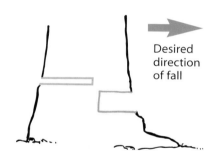

Desired direction of fall

*Box scarf

- Developed because old cross-cut saws and early chainsaws could not cut satisfactorily at an angle to the grain.
- Can be used when felling a tree with diameter more than three times greater than the length of guide bar.

Desired direction of fall

*90° scarf

- Can be used in trees with very pronounced butt swell.
- Both cuts relatively easy to match.
- Cut to such a depth that the scarf width is 2/3 tree diameter.
- Usually the depth of the 90° scarf is less than the depth of a standard scarf.

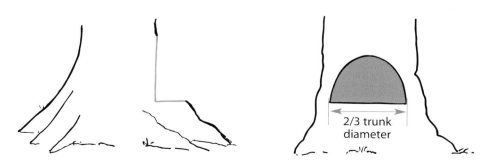

2/3 trunk diameter

Note: V Scarf, Box Scarf and 90° Scarf may be used in problem tree felling.

Size of opening

- Slope of top cut (or bottom cut) should be 30° to 45°. This is to create an opening to control the tree's fall through as large an angle as possible.
- If opening is too narrow, then scarf closes soon after the tree begins to fall, thus breaking holding wood too early.

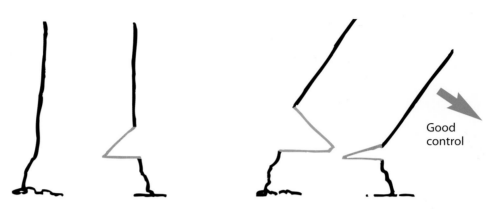

Good control

Cuts meet exactly

- Don't overcut on top or bottom cuts.
- Ensure the holding wood is not cut.
- Allow tree to fall through full angle of scarf, rather than sitting on overcut and prematurely breaking holding wood.

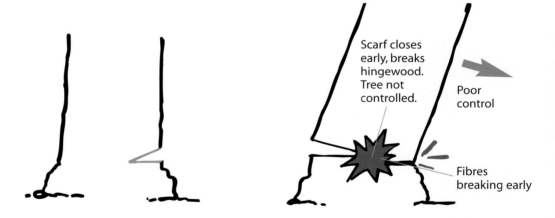

Scarf closes early, breaks hingewood. Tree not controlled.

Poor control

Fibres breaking early

Line of scarf is horizontal

- If line of scarf is not horizontal, then holding wood on higher corner will break first, thus pulling tree off line of fall.

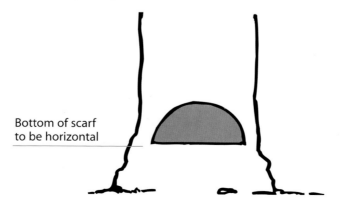

Bottom of scarf to be horizontal

Typical result of poor scarf and incorrect placement of back cut

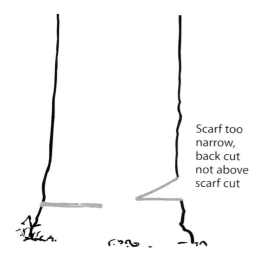

Scarf too narrow, back cut not above scarf cut

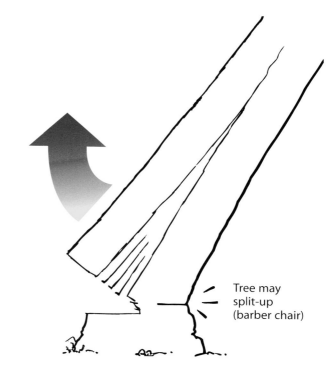

Tree may split-up (barber chair)

Tree may split-up even if the back cut is placed above scarf cut if the scarf has been cut too narrowly

Back cut (felling cut)

Characteristics of a good back cut
- Should be at least 25 mm to 50 mm above level of horizontal cut in scarf.
- As a general rule, the height of the cut above the scarf horizontal cut is approximately 50 mm for each 500 mm of tree's diameter. (50 mm minimum height.)
- Provides a step which prevents tree slipping backwards over stump (especially uphill felling).
- Prevents butt log being damaged through splinters being torn out of log. (Splinters pulled out of stump.)
- Trees are harder to fall with high back cuts. This creates more holding wood to be broken. (Particularly dangerous when wedging a slightly backwards leaning tree.)
- Line of back cut should be horizontal.
- Sloping back cut will give uneven thickness in the holding wood.
- Should leave sufficient thickness of holding wood to cut with scarf to guide trees through intended fall.
- The features of the back cut are common to all types of scarfs.

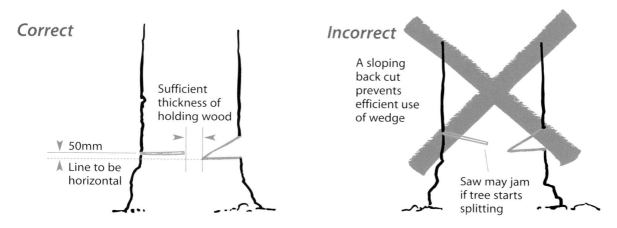

Correct

Sufficient thickness of holding wood

50mm
Line to be horizontal

Incorrect

A sloping back cut prevents efficient use of wedge

Saw may jam if tree starts splitting

Holding wood (hingewood)

- Acts as a hinge controlling the tree's fall.
- Should be approximately 10% of a solid tree's diameter – thicker if tree is defective (cross section through position of scarf).
- When felling trees against their natural lean, ensure sufficient holding wood is left on the narrow end of the taper.
- Trees with defects (pipes, etc.) holding wood needs to be slightly thicker.

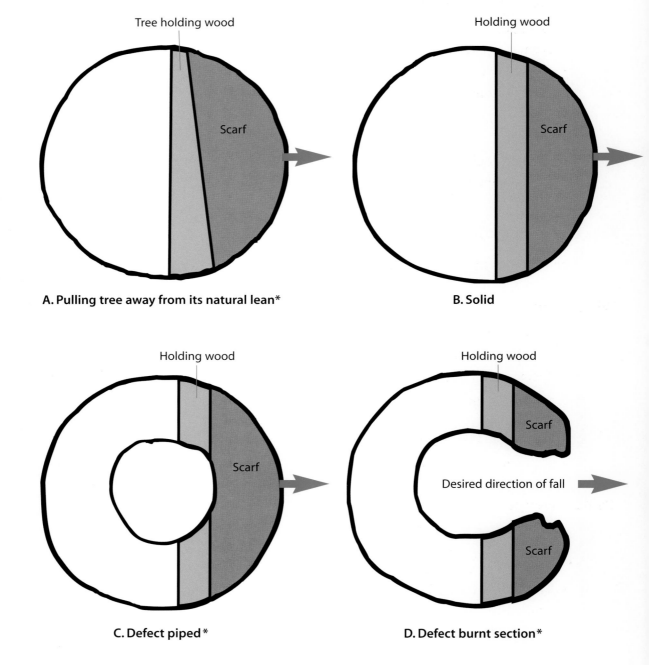

A. Pulling tree away from its natural lean*

B. Solid

C. Defect piped*

D. Defect burnt section*

***Note: (a), (c) and (d) are methods used in problem tree felling.**

Wedges

Types:

Steel
- Durable but heavy
- Will ruin chain if it contacts wedge
- Generally used to wedge large trees
- Wedge should be driven by sledge hammer

Aluminium
- Lighter than steel
- Generally won't ruin chain if chain contacts wedge
- Less durable

Plastic
- Light
- Easy on chain (chain will cut through plastic)
- More prone to damage and wear from hammer/axe blows
- Some types will 'pop' out if struck hard.

Apart from the material chosen, wedge length and lift should be chosen to suit application. (Tree species, tree size, etc.)

When used

Wedges are most often used when:
- felling slight backward leaning trees
- felling side lean trees
- cross-cutting
- heading
- preventing saw jamming
- removing jammed saw

Using a wedge

- Drive into back cut as soon as saw has cut deep enough for wedge not to come in contact with saw.
- Heavy or thick bark may have to be removed to allow edge to work on solid timber.

Wedge driven into back cut

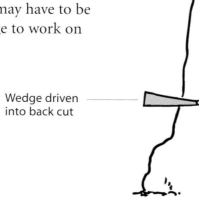

Level 3
Problem tree felling

(Advanced competence of safe chainsaw operation – harvest trees manually)

Includes the felling of trees in plantations, both softwoods and hardwoods,
as well as felling individual difficult trees.

Problem tree felling techniques

- Tree with side lean
- Tree with forward lean
- Diameter over twice cutter bar length
- Double leaders
- Defective trees – pipes, etc.
- Snags

Tree with side lean

When a tree has to be felled at an angle to its natural lean, there are 3 main techniques that can be used.

Uneven holding wood

1. Place scarf in desired direction of fall.

2. Start cutting back cut on side of natural lean.

3. Continue back cut towards opposite side of natural lean leaving thicker holding wood on that side.

The thicker holding wood will break last, thus swinging the tree towards the desired direction of fall.

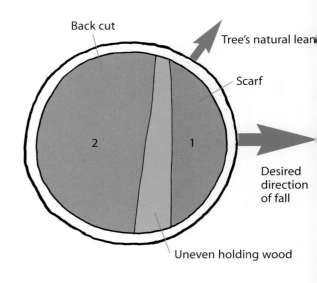

Uneven holding wood plus wedges

The technique of 'uneven holding wood' can be assisted by using a wedge in the back cut on the side of the lean. Wedge is inserted in the back cut as soon as possible and driven in gradually as the back cut proceeds.

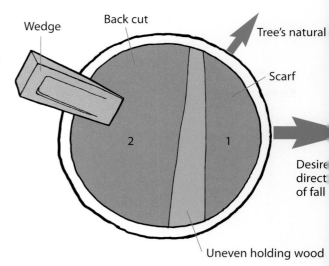

Uneven holding wood with plunge side cuts

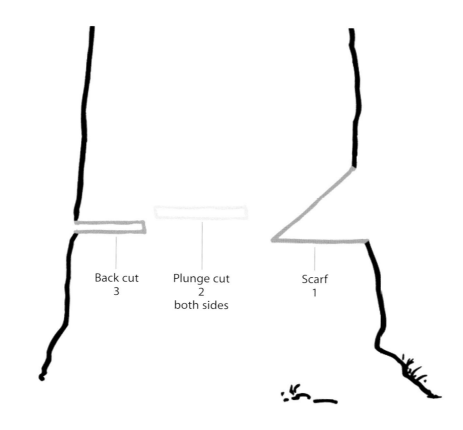

Back cut
3

Plunge cut
2
both sides

Scarf
1

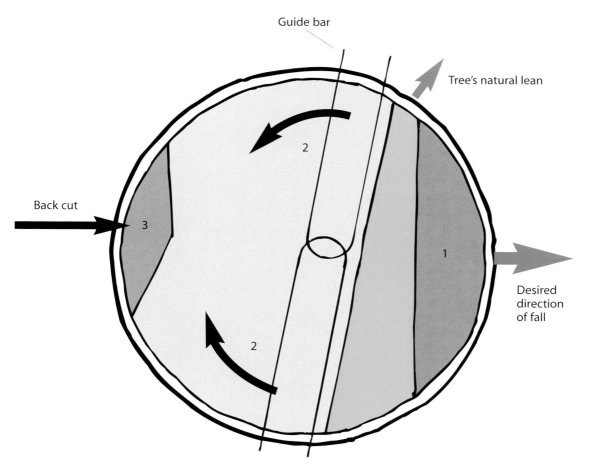

Guide bar

Tree's natural lean

Back cut

Desired
direction
of fall

Level 3

Problem tree felling

Tree with forward lean

In the case of heavily leaning trees, there is a danger of the back splitting up ('slabbing' or 'barber chairing') if the wrong cutting technique is used.

This is potentially a very dangerous situation.

Two methods can be used. All rely on the operator cutting as much as possible of the potential 'splitting wood' in an intermediate cut before the final release back cut is made.

Technique No.1

1. Standard scarf – large as possible without jamming the saw.
2. Bore in behind where holding wood is to remain.

   Cut forwards to holding wood, then backwards to leave holding strap (anchor) e.g. 150 mm thickness of timber.
3. Cut release back cut.

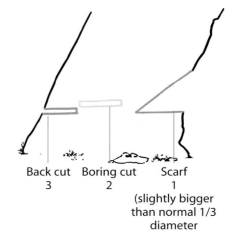

Back cut 3   Boring cut 2   Scarf 1 (slightly bigger than normal 1/3 diameter

Technique No.2

This technique is similar to technique No.1.

Instead of boring directly behind holding wood, saw is pivoted with the saw's dogs at points (a) & (b) and nosed to make cuts 2 and 3.

Holding strap 4 is cut by the release cut.

Note:

1. This technique may damage end of sawlog, i.e. pulling fibres from sawlog instead of from stump.

2. Tree will fall very rapidly following conclusion of release cut. This may not allow operator enough time to escape the required safe distance.

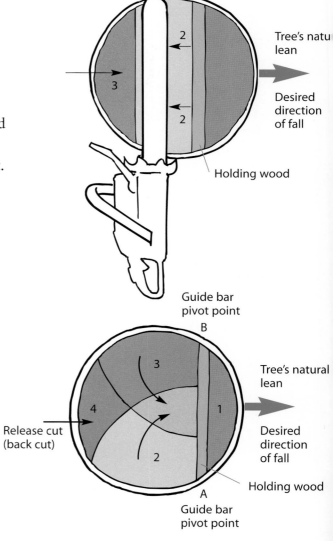

Small tree with the use of wedge or felling bar

Technique:

1. Scarf tree in normal manner – 1/4 depth.
2. Place back cut 2/3 along rear of tree.
3. Insert wedge or felling bar firmly. Heavy bark may need to be cut away around area of wedge.
4. Place release cut 12 mm below 1st back cut.
   Ensure no wood above felling cut is cut.
   Leave normal amount of holding cut.
5. Drive wedge or apply upwards pressure on felling bar to force tree to fall.

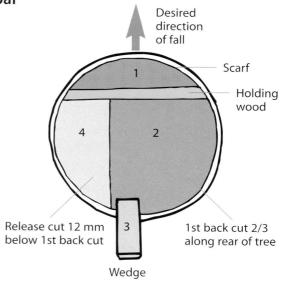

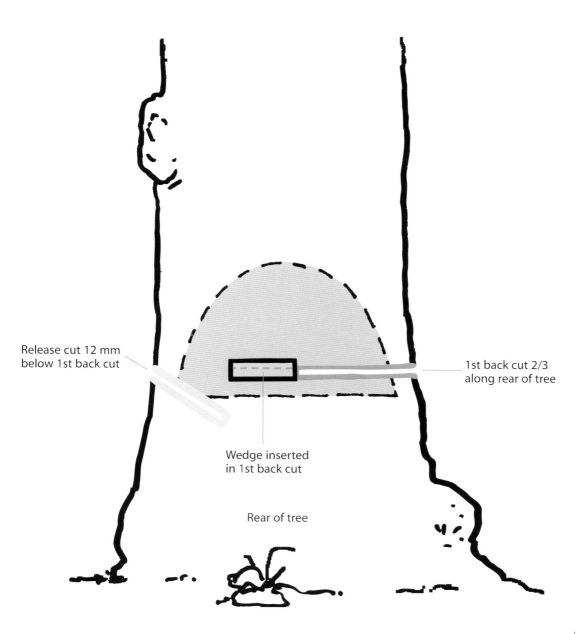

Tree diameter over twice guide bar length

1. V or Standard scarf – large as possible.

2. Make a boring cut into the centre of the scarf at the height of the intended back cut. Make this sufficiently wide so that the guide bar can reach into the cut from either side when putting in the back cut.

   As holding wood doesn't run all the way across the stump, it therefore must be wider.

3. Back cut, stand on one side and swing around to the opposite side.

Note: Cuts (2) and (3) should be on the same level. As this is fairly difficult to achieve it is suggested that the boring cut (2) be put in slightly higher than the intended back cut (3).

Ensure that cut (3) is higher than the scarf intersection point (a) by the required ratio (approximately 1:10).

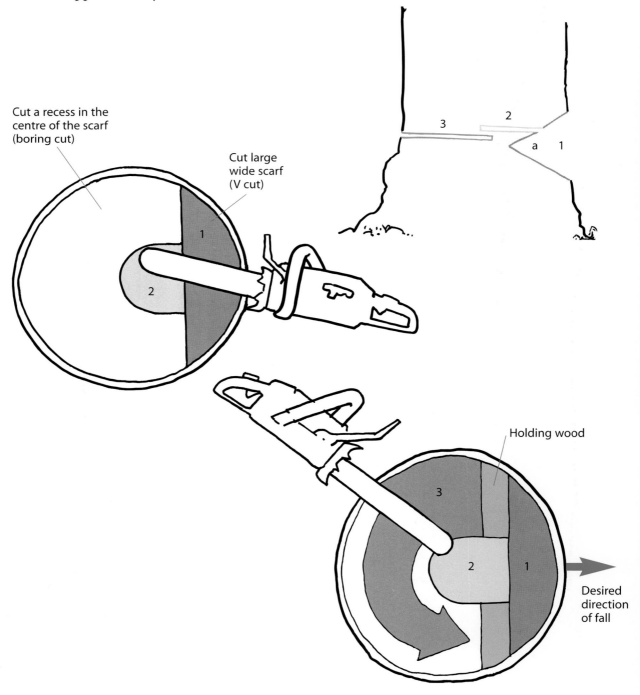

Double leader

Double leaders are often difficult to fell. It mainly depends upon where the fork begins. Frequently, even though the fork is fairly high, a weakness runs down some distance below the bottom of the fork.

If the fork is high enough, fell as a single tree, at right angles to the fork.

If it is desired to fell both trees separately below the fork line:

• Rip the joint between the trees to ensure they are separated.

• Bore in to begin back cut.

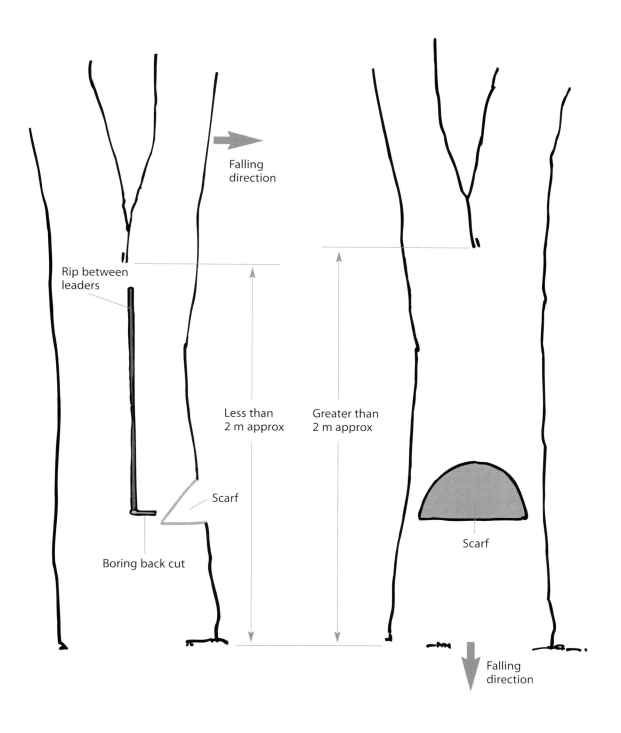

Felling 'dangerous' trees

General guidelines:
- Faller must be well-experienced and have 'Advanced Tree Felling' accreditation (Level 3).
- Faller must be willing to perform the felling operation and must consider that the felling of the dangerous tree is within their competence level.
- No faller is to be directed to fell a dangerous tree which, in the faller's opinion, is beyond their level of competence.
- If there is not enough light to clearly see the site and the drop zone of the tree being felled, then the felling must wait until daylight.

Manual tree fallers should have another experienced person checking on their welfare from outside the tree's 'drop zone', whilst felling dangerous trees. This is particularly important when felling at night, i.e. fire-fighting.

Defective trees
- Make larger than normal scarf.
- If enough solid wood - put back cut in normal manner but leave more holding wood on either side.

If in doubt, bore in from either side leaving a solid hinge and cut backwards leaving a strap of holding wood at the rear. (Same technique as Forward lean.)

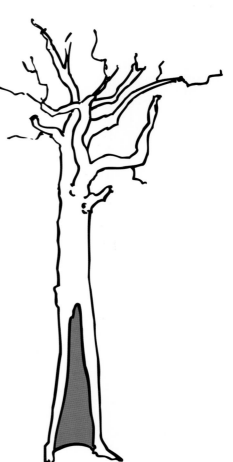

Back cut

Scarf

Direction of fall

Defect

Holding wood

Snags (stags)
- A snag is usually a dead or severely damaged tree that may cause a problem in a bushfire or high wind situation.
- Depth of scarf is increased. (Up to 50% of tree's diameter in reasonably sound trees.)
- Don't overcut scarf.
- Place back cut lower than normal.
- Take extra care when wedging.

Note: Extreme care should be taken when assessing a dead tree. Felling of this type of tree should only be carried out by very competent fallers.

Felling defective trees

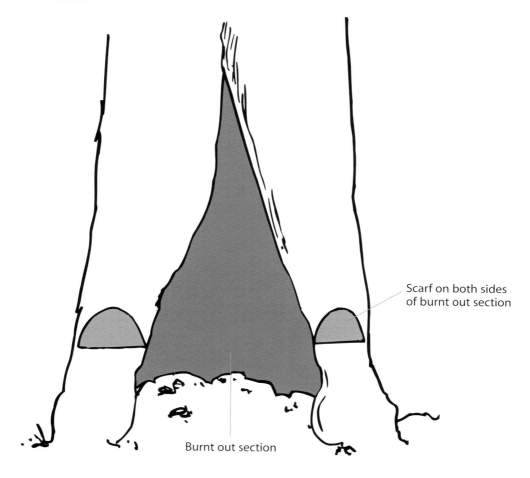

Scarf on both sides of burnt out section

Burnt out section

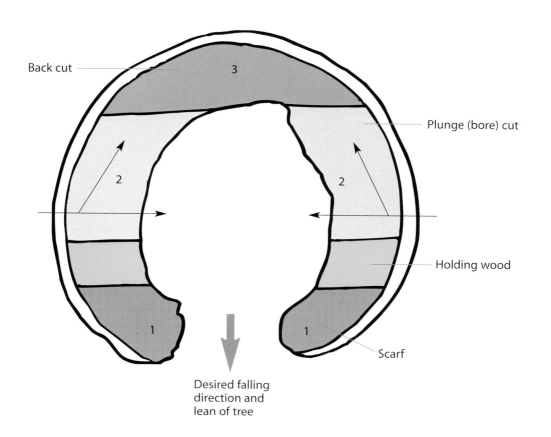

Back cut

Plunge (bore) cut

Holding wood

Scarf

Desired falling direction and lean of tree

Wind blow

Felling technique for wind break still attached to stump

Felling this type of tree with a chainsaw may be dangerous. Safest method is to push the tree over using a tractor or other suitable machinery.

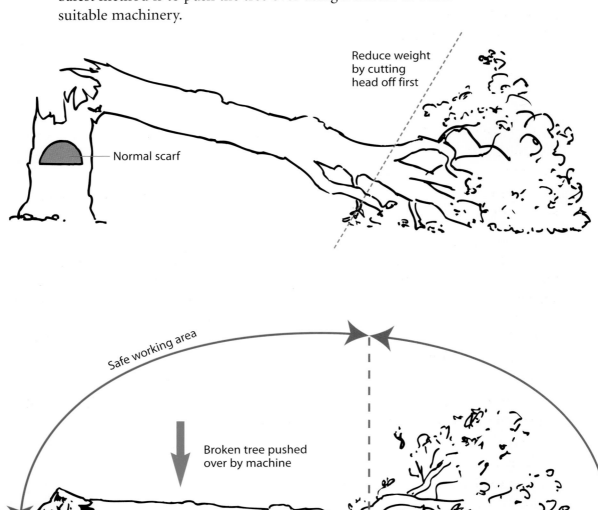

Reduce weight by cutting head off first

Normal scarf

Safe working area

Broken tree pushed over by machine

Danger zone

Manual felling hung-up trees (lodged trees)

In principle, trees that are hung-up should be grounded with the aid of machinery, i.e. log snigger or plantation harvesting equipment.

A tree faller must flag a hung-up tree immediately it has occurred.

After two (2) trees have been flagged (in any one operation) felling must cease and effort be directed to ground all hung-up trees.

Removal of tree lying across a road/track

Removing a tree supported at both ends, lying across a road and elevated at up to shoulder height is similar to a Log Trap bind but is treated in a similar manner to a Side Bind. This is due to the height that the fallen tree is lying from the ground i.e. operator would be working at shoulder height or higher.

This type of obstacle is best removed by using a combination of a chainsaw and a winch or heavy plant.

Safe work procedure

If the fallen tree is lying across a road/track and is at a height of up to shoulder heightoff the ground, then it is best for the chainsaw operator to work off the back of a truck, ute etc. Alternatively, the chainsaw operator will have to walk along the top of the fallen tree to the mid-point where the chainsaw cuts are to be placed. If this method is adopted, great care should be exercised by the chainsaw operator to ensure that they do not over balance.

- At this stage, do not cut off the tree's head or butt from the tree
- Winch rope is placed around the tree roughly along side the intended location of the scarf and paid out in the direction of pull
- A large vertical 'V' scarf is cut mid-way along tree. Scarf can be up to 1/2 a tree's diameter
- A vertical back cut (release cut) is cut directly to the 'V' leaving sufficient holding wood.
- Chainsaw operator moves away to a safe location
- Winch line is tensioned causing the tree to break.
- Separate portions of the tree are removed using normal cross-cutting techniques.

Machine assisted manual tree felling

Dangerous/problem trees that can't be safely felled by using the manual tree felling method, can be felled by using a combination of a chainsaw with the assistance of a heavy machine.

It should be noted:

1. Problem trees include trees that are to be felled away from their natural lean e.g. trees being felled along drainage lines, power lines, fence lines.
2. Machine assisted manual tree felling should only be attempted by very experienced operators holding advanced chainsaw qualifications and have experienced working with machinery.
3. Patience is required as the use of these methods should not be rushed.

4. Appreciation of the tree's lean, shape and surrounding terrain must be taken into account as each tree may present its own particular problems requiring variation to these guidelines.

5. Both operators (chainsaw and machine) should discuss the felling process prior to attempting the process.

There are two methods to fell a tree using a line:

- Line pull
- Line guide

Suitable machinery:

- Skidder
- Crawler tractor
- Machine must be fitted with certified FOPS/ROPS/OPS canopy

Suitable pulling line:

- Wire snigging rope
- Logging chain

Line pull

This method is used to fell a tree directly against its natural lean. (180° away from its natural lean.)

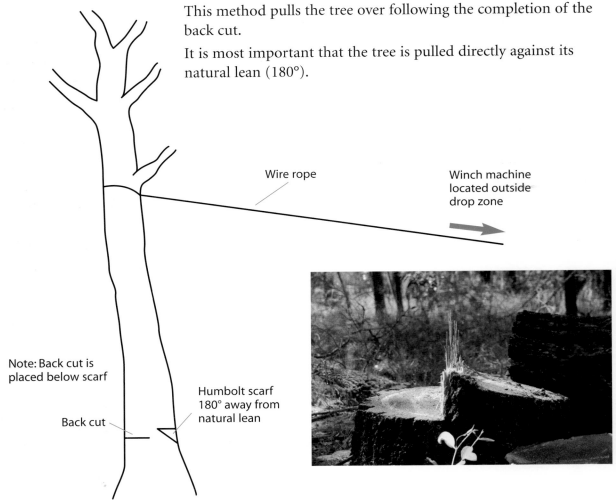

This method pulls the tree over following the completion of the back cut.

It is most important that the tree is pulled directly against its natural lean (180°).

Wire rope

Winch machine located outside drop zone

Note: Back cut is placed below scarf

Back cut

Humbolt scarf 180° away from natural lean

The combination of the humbolt scarf together with the back cut placed below the line of scarf ensures that the machine does not pull the tree off it's stump.

Safe work procedure

- Tree's natural lean is determined
- The direction of fall must be 180° away from the tree's natural lean
- Machine (winch) is positioned along desired direction of fall, beyond tree's length
- Wire is secured around tree, as high as possible
- Escape route is prepared
- Wire is tensioned to just take the weight of the tree
- Scarf is cut (approx 1/4 to 1/3 diameter) facing desired direction of fall
- Tension on wire is maintained
- Back cut is placed below line of scarf and sufficient holding wood is retained
- Chainsaw operator retreats along escape route
- Chainsaw operator signals winch operator to increase tension on wire. When felling smaller trees, the machine can drive forward instead of using the winch.
- Tree falls in desired direction of fall

Line guide

This method is used to fell a tree up to approx 80° away from its natural lean.

This method pulls the tree up to its balance point and holds the tree there, enabling the tree to fall in the direction of the scarf. The tensioned wire rope holds the tree whilst it is falling, thus guiding the direction of fall.

The position of the machine (winch) is critical. The wire must not pull the tree at 90° to its natural lean as there is a danger that the tree could fall backwards when it is being supported at its balance point. The machine must not be positioned greater than 80° from the direction of natural lean. 65° to 75° away from the desired direction of fall is best.

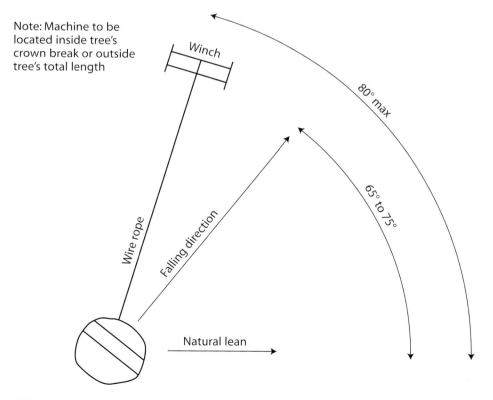

Note: Machine to be located inside tree's crown break or outside tree's total length

Care should be exercised to ensure that the pressure on the line is maintained during the initial stages of the tree's fall.

Safe work procedure

- Tree's natural lean is determined
- Tree's desired direction of fall is determined. Up to 80° away from the tree's natural lean
- For best results, machine (tractor) is located approx 65° to 75° away from, but in the direction of the desired direction of fall. Machine can be positioned inside the tree's crown break or outside the total length of the tree
- Escape route prepared
- Wire is secured around tree as high as possible
- Wire is tensioned to just take the weight of the tree
- Scarf is cut (approx 1/4 to 1/3 diameter) facing desired direction of fall
- Tension on rope is maintained to take the weight of the tree
- Back cut is placed.
- Sufficient holding wood is retained
- Chainsaw operator retreats along escape route
- Chainsaw operator signals the winch operator to increase tension on rope to bring the tree up to its balance point
- Tree begins to fall, tension on wire is maintained to guide the tree through the first part of its fall
- Tree falls in desired direction of fall.

IMPORTANT

The procedure used to fell a tree using this method must remain totally under the control of the chainsaw operator.

The machine operator takes their instructions from the chainsaw operator.

Chainsaw operator must be away from the tree before the wire is tensioned or tension is adjusted.

Pushing tree over with a crawler tractor – dozer blade

Other heavy plant can be used to push a tree over utilising this method:

- Rubber-tyred skidder
- Rear-end hydraulic equipment e.g. grapple, ripper frame.
- Hydraulic excavator

This method can be employed to fell trees that are required to be felled away from the tree's natural lean.

Safe work procedure

- Normal scarf is cut, facing desired direction of fall.
- Tractor's dozer blade is placed against the tree to just take the weight of the tree.
  - Blade is not extended to its maximum height
  - It may be necessary for a earth ramp to be pushed up to gain addition height of push.
- Back cut is cut **below** scarf, leaving normal holding wood.
  Note: if back cut is cut above the scarf, there is a danger that the tractor may push the tree off its stump thus allowing the tree to fall in an uncontrolled manner.
  In this case there is a real possibility of the tree falling back over the tractor.

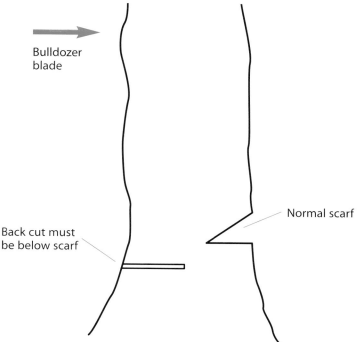

Bulldozer blade

Normal scarf

Back cut must be below scarf

Pushing tree over with a crawler tractor

- Chainsaw operator moves away from the tree along prepared escape route
- Tractor applies full power (steady push) and pushes tree over.
  - It is important that when full power is applied the blade is also extended to its maximum height.
  - This helps to exert a downward pressure on the tractor's tracks thus increasing traction.
  - It may be necessary for the tractor to have a number of attempts to push the tree over but great care must be exercised not to take the weight off the tree until it is committed to fall.

It is recommended that wedge/s be placed in the backcut for should the machine fail to push the tree over, it may be necessary for the chainsaw operator to extend the backcut. Care should be exercised to prevent the need for the chainsaw operator to work directly under the machine at this critical stage.

Tree jacking

This method can be employed to fell trees that are required to be felled directly against the direction of their natural lean i.e. 180° away from the tree's natural lean.

This method should only be used on trees that are reasonably sound and free from decay, particularly in the area where the felling cuts and jacks will be placed.

The method outlined must be seen as a general guideline. Each individual tree may present its own particular problems requiring a variation in the method described.

Points to note:

1. Tree jacking should only be attempted by very experienced operators holding advanced chainsaw qualifications and who are trained in the use of tree jacks.
2. It is normal for two operators to be employed, one using the chainsaw and the other operating the jack.
3. This method can employ one or two jacks working in combination, it depends upon the size of the tree to be jacked.

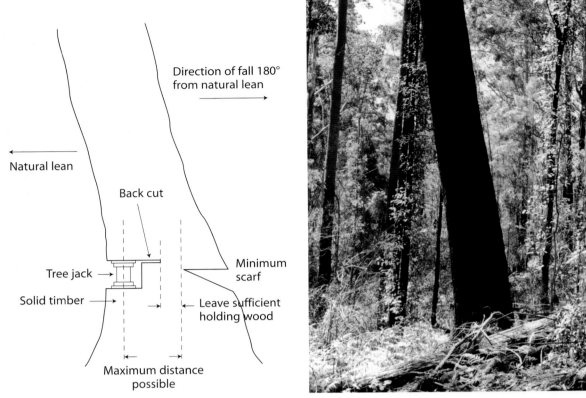

Jacking tree 180° away from its natural lean

Tree jacks in place

Scarf in place and back cut (extension of jack slot) in place

Safe work procedure

- Determine the desired direction of fall. This must be directly against the tree's natural lean.
- Escape route must be prepared
- Cut in jack slot ensuring a snug fit with the closed jack/s. Over-cut top cut by at least guide bar width. This will become the start of the future back cut. It is important that the vertical cut does not extend beyond the two horizontal cuts.

Tree committed to fall and operators have retreated along escape route

Note timber packing under the jacks to give additional lift

- Insert jack/s and apply pressure to 1/4 capacity. Jack/s should be placed to achieve a maximum distance between centre of jack and the start of the holding wood. Ensure that the jack's base is fully inserted in the slot.

- Cut minimum scarf in the normal manner (simple tree felling) leaving sufficient holding wood. The intersection of scarf cuts must be below future back cut. Jack pressure is increased to 3/4 capacity.

- Extend back cut (top of jack slot) to leave sufficient holding wood as continuous pressure is applied to jacks making sure the maximum rated pressure is not exceeded.

  A close watch must be kept on the jack's pressure gauge whilst the back cut is being cut. This will assist in reading how the tree is behaving i.e. a fall in pressure will mean the tree is being influenced by the jack and is moving away from its natural lean.

  This is a slow process and should not be rushed.

- Upon completion of the back cut, full pressure is applied to the jack/s ensuring that the jack is not over pressurised.

- It may be necessary to place timber packing under the jack to increase its jacking height. This can only be done when using two jacks in tandem.

- When tree is committed to fall, operator/s leave the tree via the prepared escape route.

Level 3

Tree jacking

Competencies for safe chainsaw operation

Forest and Forest Products Industry Training Package

Level 1

FPIC2007A Maintain chainsaws

This unit describes the work involved in the cleaning, checking and adjustment of the saw and the sharpening of the chain.

Suggested Pre-Requisites

FPI OHS 1A   Follow defined OHS policies and procedures

Clean and check saw components

1) OHS regulations, policies and procedures relevant to maintaining chainsaws are to be followed throughout the application of this competency
2) Sawchain and chainsaw body are cleaned and inspected to determine condition
3) Air filter is removed, cleaned, checked and replaced or reinserted
4) Spark plug is removed, condition checked and replaced or reinserted
5) Sawchain tension is checked and adjusted as required

Check and adjust sawchain

1) Guards/bars are loosened/removed to provide access to adjustment
2) Tension is adjusted to specification
3) Guards/bars are replaced to manufacturer's instructions

Replace worn sawchain/depth gauges

1) Each cutting edge of sawchain is checked for condition
2) Worn sprocket/sawchain is replaced to manufacturer's instructions

Sharpen sawchain

1) Chainsaw is set-up in position for filling/grinding
2) Each sawchain cutting edge is sharpened to manufacturer's instructions

Range of variables

- Sharpening methods may include grinding and hand filing
- Chainsaws may have a range of engine types
- OHS requirements include manual handling, use of protective clothing and safety equipment, machine guarding, operation of equipment and site safety policies and procedures

Evidence guide

Underpinning knowledge
Explains:
- OHS regulations, policies and procedures for maintaining chainsaws
- Various types of chainsaws and uses
- Chainsaw maintenance procedures
- The importance of accuracy

Underpinning skills
Demonstrates ability to:
- Safely and effectively maintain chainsaws
- Apply chainsaw maintenance procedures and techniques
- Locate, interpret and apply relevant information
- Convey information in oral form

Critical aspects of evidence
Assessment must confirm the application of appropriate knowledge and skills to:
- Safely maintain chainsaws
- Communicate effectively with others in associated areas
- Clean and check components
- Check and adjust sawchain
- Replace worn sawchain
- Sharpen sawchain

Independent assessment of unit
This unit of competency may be assessed in conjunction with other units which form part of a job task

Assessment context
This unit may be assessed in the workplace or under conditions which accurately simulate a realistic workplace

FPIH2001A Trim and cross-cut felled trees – Production

This unit of competency describes the work involved in the trimming and cutting of felled trees with a chainsaw to produce logs.

Suggested Pre-Requisites

FPI OHS 1A	Follow defined OHS policies and procedures
FP G41A	Use hand-held tools

Identify cross-cutting requirements
1) OHS regulations, policies and procedures relevant to trimming and cross-cutting harvested trees are to be followed throughout the application of the competency
2) Felled trees to be prepared are identified and confirmed in accordance with site procedures
3) Requirements. Lengths and specifications for finished logs are identified from orders, or site procedures

4) Industry and government standards are recognised and applied in planning cutting

5) Communication with others involved with the work is established and maintained to ensure efficient work flow co-ordination, personnel co-operation and safety throughout the application of this competency

Prepare and maintain equipment

1) Chainsaw and component options suitable for planned cutting are selected and prepared

2) Chainsaw is checked to relevant standards prior to use

3) Required support tools, protective equipment, first aid gear, spares, maintenance requirements and fuel are selected, prepared, carried and positioned to minimise cutting delays

4) Characteristics of blunt or damaged sawchain are recognised

5) Suitability of chainsaw set up is assessed with changing cutting conditions

6) Sawchain is sharpened and adjusted or components changed to maintain cutting safely and productivity

Assess felled tree and plan cutting

1) Environmental conditions including ground growth, ground slope and ground hazards are identified and used to assess the cutting of each tree

2) Awareness of environmental conditions and other personnel's activity are maintained and cutting activity modified as a result of significant changes

3) Trees, locations and stability are assessed for conditions likely to affect safety of cross-cutting

4) Tree is moved or stablised for safe cutting in accordance with site standards and regulations

5) Tree is visually assessed for defects, grade and recovery or results of previous assessment identified

6) Cutting pattern is selected to maximise volume and quality of recovery in accordance with assessments, finished log specifications, and order requirements

7) Sequence of cross-cutting is planned to maintain control of cut sections and minimise cutting problems

8) Cutting positions selected safisfy order requirements and industry standard lengths

9) Cutting positions are accurately measured and marked

10) Cut logs are suitable for extraction and/or transport considering methods used, site conditions and specific log location

11) Debris likely to cause saw damage during trimming or cutting is cleared from tree surface

12) Trees which cannot be safely cut are identified and referred to others

Trim and cross-cut felled trees

1) Accessible branches and knots are trimmed to requirements and specifications

2) Head of tree is removed in accordance with minimum diameter, damage, shape and known length requirements

3) Slash is regularly cleared from tree and work site to allow access for cutting or movement

4) Tree section on each side of planned cut is secured or potential movement recognised and planned for

5) Individual cross-cut is planned to optimise time and safety

6) Chainsaw is operated and tree cut in accordance with safety standards applicable to site conditions

7) Cutting techniques is adjusted in response to movement and condition of tree

8) Unexpected characteristics of tree are identified and planning reviewed

9) Wedges are used as required to assist cutting

10) Cutting procedures minimise capping and splitting of logs

11) Cuts are within site and customer standard tolerances for length and angle relative to log centre line

12) Cross-cut is completed once initiated

13) Logs are prepared to assist extraction in accordance with site requirements and methods

Range of variables

- Trees may be softwood or hardwood
- Trees may be of any size and condition which can be safely trimmed and cross-cut
- Cross-cutting may be undertaken in all conditions for which it is safe including slopes up to the maximum allowed by relevant regulations
- Trees may be trimmed and cross-cut at site of falling (before extraction) or on landing (after extraction)
- Logs prepared may be for peeling, sawing or pulp
- Assessment for grade and recovery is as specified in site requirements
- Assessment of tree and location includes stresses, ground conditions, slope, tree support, compression of branches, hazards from other logs or ground obstacles
- Defects to be found when assessing prior to cutting include splits, falling damage, fire damage, infestation, pipe, shake, twist and branch/knot locations
- OHS regulations include Codes of Practice and AS2727 and requirements include availability of correct first aid kit, erection of warning signs, wearing of required personal protection including head, eye, ear, cut-proof leg protection, safety footwear and high visibility vest, manual handling requirements, maintenance of safe forest practices including location of other people and potential falling objects, required actions relating to forest fire, working alone requirements, recognition of hazards and required actions in bush and tree falling, procedures for cross-cutting on slopes, acceptable cutting positions and the use of approved containers for fuel and oil

Evidence guide

Underpinning knowledge
Explains:

- OHS Regulations, policies and procedures for trimming and cross-cutting harvested trees
- All safety and environmental requirements for operation in forest settings
- The processes of assessment, planning, trimming and cross-cutting for the range of routinely available trees and conditions

- The planning related to work site requirements and extraction methods
- The importance of accuracy
- The purpose of record keeping

Underpinning skills
Demonstrates the ability to:

- Safely operate the chainsaw equipment over the full range of processes for trimming and cross-cutting felled trees
- Locate, interpret and apply relevant information
- Convey information in oral form
- Interpret and apply common industry terminology
- Apply safety and environmental requirements for operations in forest settings
- Assess, plan, trim and cross-cut trees
- Plan work site requirements and extraction methods
- Optimise recovery over a number of trees with regard to volume, grade and order requirements
- Prepare and communicate requirements

Critical aspects of evidence
Assessment must confirm the application of appropriate knowledge and skills to:

- Safely trim and cross-cut felled trees
- Communicate effectively with others in associated areas
- Identify and confirm cross-cutting requirements
- Prepare and maintain equipment
- Assess felled trees and plan cutting
- Trim felled trees using a chainsaw
- Cross-cut trees using a chainsaw

Independent assessment of units
This unit of competency may be assessed in conjunction with other units which form part of a job role

Assessment context
This unit may be assessed in the workplace or under conditions which accurately simulate a realistic workplace

Note: Permits required by regulation or site requirements, to authorise the operation for assessment purposes, are to be obtained

FPIH2003A Harvest trees manually – Basic

This unit describes the work involved in the preparation, planning and the manual chainsaw harvesting of trees, at the basic level

Suggested Pre-Requisites

FPI OHS 1A	Follow defined OHS policies and procedures
FPIH2001A	Trim and cross-cut felled trees (production)
FP G41A	Use hand-held tools

1) OHS regulations. Policies and procedures relevant to the manual falling of trees are to be followed throughout the application of this competency
2) General factors affecting falling requirements and specific forest/site hazards are identified and confirmed with supervisor
3) Specific trees to be felled and retained are identified in accordance with site procedures
4) Working face and general falling direction are identified and confirmed
5) Falling sequence for individual trees is planned to minimize danger, damage and extraction problems
6) Communication with others involved with the work is established and maintained to ensure efficient work flow co-ordination, personnel co-operation and safety throughout the application of this competency

Prepare and maintain falling equipment

1) Chainsaw and component options suitable for planned falling are selected and prepared
2) Chainsaw is checked to relevant standards prior to use
3) Required support tools, protective equipment, first aid gear, spares, maintenance requirements and fuel are selected, prepared, carried and positioned to minimize falling delays
4) Characteristics of blunt or damaged sawchain are recognised
5) Sawchain is sharpened and adjusted or components changed to maintain falling safety and productivity

Apply environmental protection measures

1) Environmental conditions including ground growth, canopy, general forest lean, ground slope, ground hazards, wind speed and direction, fallen trees and density of trees are identified and used to assess the falling of each tree
2) Awareness of environmental conditions and other personnel's activity are maintained and falling activity modified as a result of significant changes
3) Legal and other environmental protection measures, including those related to soil and water protection, are identified and applied

Assess tree and plan falling

1) Trees which are beyond the characteristics appropriate for basic manual harvesting are referred to others
2) Tree is visually assessed for falling characteristics
3) Direction required for falling and degree of error allowable are identified considering hung-ups, damage and extraction

4) Trees which cannot be safely felled with own skills are identified and referred to others

5) Trees considered too dangerous to fall are marked in accordance with relevant national and state or territory forest safety codes

6) Sequence of cuts to fall tree is planned to meet standard falling procedures

Prepare surroundings

1) Most suitable escape route is selected and cleared of growth and other obstacles

2) Preparation meets environmental care principles and statutory body requirements

3) Location of other personnel is noted and monitored

Fall tree

1) Scarf is cut to plan in accordance with standard of accuracy

2) Unexpected characteristics of tree are identified and planning reviewed

3) Help is requested if cuts made may lead to loss of control of tree in falling

4) Backcut/s is/are made to provide planned hinge-wood and maintain control of tree

5) Cutting technique is adjusted in response to movement and condition of tree

6) Wedges are used to control movement and direction of falling

7) Falling is completed once initiated

8) Planned escape route is used when tree starts to fall

9) Fall of tree and movement on ground are monitored until tree is stable

10) Trees which hang-up are immediately cleared or marked and assistance requested

Range of variables

• Trees will be fallen in a forest environment and may require a range of cuts

• Trees fallen during basic harvesting are to conform with the following characteristics:

– diameter not more than 50 cm at position of cut

– height not more than 20 m

– species and growth conditions not prone to twisting or splitting

– sound wood condition in barrel

– single leader

– lean and weight distribution consistent with falling direction

• Conditions in which falling will be undertaken may include:

– minimal canopy affecting free fall

– ground slope not excessive

– wind not significantly affecting falling characteristics

– absence of ground growth or fallen trees preventing complete fall

– absence of stags and hazardous ground features in falling radius

– clear falling or sparse tree density

– absence of ground growth or fallen trees preventing free movement around tree stump

• General factors identified includes trees to be felled and retained, extraction methods, processing location and environmental care principles

• Visual assessment of tree covers size, weight distribution, lean, species, multiple leaders, soundness of timber, growth characteristics and stresses

• Clearance for assessment and provision of escape route may require assistance from dozer or other machine

- OHS regulations include Codes of Practice and SA2727 and requirements include carrying of correct first aid kit, erection of warning signs, wearing of required personal protection including head, eye, ear, cut-proof leg protection, safety footwear and high visibility vest, manual handling requirements, maintenance of safe forest practices including location of other people and potential falling objects, required actions relating to forest fire, working alone requirements, recognition of hazards and required actions in bush and tree falling and use of approved containers for fuel and oil

Evidence guide

Underpinning knowledge

Explains:

- OHS regulations, policies and procedures for the manual falling of trees
- All safety and environmental requirements for operation in forest settings
- Limitations in conditions and trees for falling
- Process of assessment, planning and falling for the range of trees and conditions
- The selection and maintenance of appropriate equipment
- The preparation and communication which maintains efficient falling
- The importance of accuracy
- The purpose of record keeping

Underpinning skills

Demonstrates the ability to:

- Safely operate chainsaw equipment and material over the full range of processes for the basic manual felling of trees
- Apply safety and environmental requirements for operation in forest settings
- Locate, interpret and apply relevant information
- Convey information in oral form
- Select appropriate mathematical processes
- Interpret and apply common industry terminology
- Understand limitations in conditions and trees for falling
- Assess, plan and fall the range of trees under normal conditions
- Select and maintain appropriate equipment
- Prepare and communicate to maintain efficient falling

Critical aspects of evidence

Assessment must confirm the application of appropriate knowledge and skills to:

- Safely harvest trees (basic)
- Communicate effectively with others in associated areas
- Apply mathematical procedures such as estimation and measurement
- Identify falling requirements
- Prepare and maintain falling equipment
- Apply environmental protection measures
- Assess tree
- Plan felling
- Fall tree

Independent assessment of units
This unit will normally be assessed as a discrete/stand alone competency

Assessment context
This unit may be assessed in the workplace or under conditions which accurately simulate a realistic workplace

FPIH3020A Harvest trees manually – Intermediate

This unit describes the work involved in the preparation, planning and the manual chainsaw harvesting of trees, at the intermediate level

Suggested Pre-Requisites

FPI OHS 1A	Follow defined OHS policies and procedures
FPIH2003A	Harvest trees manually basic
FP G41A	Use hand-held tools

Plan falling sequence

1) OHS regulations, policies and procedures relevant to manual felling of trees are to be followed throughout the application of this competency
2) General factors affecting falling requirements and specific forest/site hazards are identified
3) Trees to be felled and retained are identified from general coupe/compartment and environmental requirements, site plan and environmental features
4) Log extraction method and associated requirements for landings and snig tracks or cable anchor points are recognised
5) Working face and general falling direction are identified
6) Falling sequence for individual trees is progressively planned to meet general requirements, minimise danger and maximise falling and extraction efficiency
7) Communication with others involved with the work is established and maintained to ensure efficient work flow co-ordination, personnel co-operation and safety throughout the application of this competency

Prepare and maintain falling equipment

1) Chainsaw and component options suitable for planned falling are selected and prepared
2) Chainsaw is checked to relevant standards prior to use
3) Required support tools, protective equipment, first aid gear, spares, maintenance requirements and fuel are selected, prepared, carried and positioned to minimise falling delays
4) Characteristics of blunt or damaged sawchain are recognised
5) Suitability of chainsaw set up is assessed with changing falling conditions
6) Sawchain is sharpened and adjusted or components changed to maintain and improve falling safety and productivity

Apply environmental protection measures

1) Environmental conditions including ground growth, canopy, general forest lean, ground slope, ground hazards, wind speed and direction, fallen trees and density of trees are identified and used to assess the falling of each tree
2) Awareness of environmental conditions and other personnel's activity are maintained and falling activity modified as a result of significant changes
3) Legal and other environmental protection measures, including those related to soil and water protection, are identified and applied

Assess tree and plan falling

1) Trees which are beyond the characteristics appropriate to intermediate manual harvesting are referred to others
2) Growth is cleared to enable visual assessment of tree to be felled
3) Tree is visually assessed for falling characteristics
4) Direction required for falling and degree of error allowable are identified considering hung-ups, damage and extraction
5) Trees which cannot be safely felled with own skills are identified and referred to others
6) Trees considered too dangerous to fall are marked in accordance with relevant national and state or territory forest safety codes
7) Sequence of cuts to fall tree is planned to control direction of fall and minimise splitting

Prepare surroundings

1) Most suitable escape route is selected and cleared of growth and other obstacles
2) Preparation meets environmental care principles and statutory body requirements
3) Location of other personnel is noted and monitored

Fall tree

1) Scarf is cut to plan in accordance with standard of accuracy
2) Unexpected characteristics of tree are identified and planning reviewed
3) Help is requested if cuts made may lead to loss of control of tree in falling
4) Backcut/s is/are made to provide planned hinge-wood and maintain control of tree
5) Cutting technique is adjusted in response to movement and condition of tree
6) Wedges are used to control movement and direction of falling
7) Falling is completed once initiated
8) Planned escape route is used when tree starts to fall
9) Fall of tree and movement on ground are monitored until tree is stable
10) Trees which hang-up are immediately cleared or marked and assistance requested

Range of variables

• Trees fallen during intermediate harvesting are to conform with the following characteristics:
  – diameter not more than 80 cm at position of cut
  – height not more than 40 m
  – sound wood condition in barrel
  – lean and weight distribution which can be adapted to falling direction with the use of wedges and/or control with hinge-wood
• Falling may require the use of multiple cuts
• Conditions in which falling will be undertaken may include:
  – Ground slope not more than 20 degrees
  – Moderate wind speed
  – Ground is clear of growth or fallen trees which may prevent complete fall
  – Absence of other trees and hazardous ground features within planned line of fall

- General factors identified includes trees to be felled and retained, extraction methods, processing location and environmental care principles
- Environmental requirements include those relating to gullies, water courses and seed and habitat trees
- Visual assessment of tree covers size, weight distribution, lean, species, multiple leaders, soundness of timber, growth characteristics and stresses
- Clearance for assessment and provision of escape route may require assistance from dozer or other machine
- OHS regulations include Codes of Practice and SA2727 and requirements include carrying of correct first aid kit, erection of warning signs, wearing of required personal protection including head, eye, ear, cut-proof leg protection, safety footwear and high visibility vest, manual handling requirements, maintenance of safe forest practices including location of other people and potential falling objects, required actions relating to forest fire, working alone requirements, recognition of hazards and required actions in bush and tree falling and use of approved containers for fuel and oil

Evidence guide

Underpinning knowledge
Explains:
- OHS regulations, policies and procedures for the manual falling of trees
- All safety and environmental requirements for operation in forest settings
- Limitations in conditions and trees for falling
- Process of assessment, planning and falling for the trees and conditions including control of falling direction consistent with this range
- Planning related to worksite requirements and extraction methods
- The preparation and communication which maintains efficient falling
- The importance of accuracy
- The purpose of record keeping

Underpinning skills
Demonstrates the ability to:
- Safely and effectively operate chainsaw equipment and material over the full range of processes for the intermediate manual felling of trees
- Locate, interpret and apply relevant information in written, diagrammatic and/or oral form
- Convey information in written and/or oral form
- Select appropriate mathematical processes
- Understand limitations in conditions and trees for falling
- Assess, plan and fall within the range of variables for trees and conditions including control of falling direction consistent with this range
- Plan work to site requirements and extraction methods
- Prepare and communicate to maintain efficient falling

Critical aspects of evidence
Assessment must confirm the application of appropriate knowledge and skills to:
- Safely harvest trees (intermediate)

- Communicate effectively with others in associated areas
- Apply mathematical procedures such as estimation and measurement
- Access, interpret, assess and apply technical information
- Plan falling sequence
- Prepare and maintain falling equipment
- Apply environmental protection measures
- Assess tree
- Prepare surrounds
- Fall tree

Independent assessment of units

This unit will normally be assessed as a discrete/stand alone competency

Assessment context

This unit may be assessed in the workplace or under conditions which accurately simulate a realistic workplace

Level 3

FPIH3041A Harvest trees manually – Advanced

This unit describes the work involved in the preparation, planning and the manual chainsaw harvesting of trees, at the advanced level

Suggested Pre-Requisites

FPI OHS 1A	Follow defined OHS policies and procedures
FPIH3020A	Harvest trees manually – Intermediate

Plan falling sequence

1) OHS regulations, policies and procedures relevant to manual felling of trees are to be followed throughout the application of this competency
2) General factors affecting falling requirements and specific forest/site hazards are identified
3) Trees to be felled and retained are identified from general coupe/compartment and environmental requirements, site plan and environmental features
4) Log extraction method and associated requirements for landings and snig tracks or cable anchor points are recognised
5) General falling direction and working face are planned to minimise danger, damage and extraction problems
6) Falling sequence for individual trees is progressively planned to meet general requirements, minimise danger and maximise falling and extraction efficiency
7) Communication with others involved with the work is established and maintained to ensure efficient work flow co-ordination, personnel co-operation and safety throughout the application of this competency

Prepare and maintain falling equipment

1) Chainsaw and component options suitable for planned falling are selected and prepared
2) Chainsaw is checked to relevant standards prior to use
3) Required support tools, protective equipment, first aid gear, spares, maintenance requirements and fuel are selected, prepared, carried and positioned to minimize falling delays
4) Characteristics of blunt or damaged sawchain are recognised
5) Suitability of chainsaw set up is assessed with changing falling conditions
6) Sawchain is sharpened and adjusted or components changed to maintain and improve falling safety and productivity

Apply environmental protection measures

1) Environmental conditions including ground growth, canopy, general forest lean, ground slope, ground hazards, wind speed and direction, fallen trees and density of trees are identified and used to assess the falling of each tree
2) Awareness of environmental conditions and other personnel's activity are maintained and falling activity modified as a result of significant changes
3) Legal and other environmental protection measures, including those related to soil and water protection, are identified and applied

Assess tree and plan falling

1) Growth is cleared to enable visual assessment of tree to be felled
2) Tree is visually assessed for falling characteristics
3) Direction required for falling and degree of error allowable are identified considering hung-ups, damage and extraction
4) Trees considered too dangerous to fall are marked in accordance with relevant national and state or territory forest safety codes
5) Sequence of cuts to fall tree is planned to control direction of fall and minimize splitting including method of dealing with additional leader(s) where applicable

Prepare surroundings

1) OHS and fire safety regulations, policies and precautions are followed
2) Most suitable escape route is selected and cleared of growth and other obstacles
3) Preparation meets environmental care principles and statutory body requirements
4) Location of other personnel is noted and monitored

Fall tree

1) OHS and fire safety regulations, policies and precautions are followed
2) Additional leader(s) is/are removed and cleared in accordance with plan
3) Scarf is cut to plan in accordance with standard of accuracy
4) Unexpected characteristics of tree are identified and planning reviewed
5) Backcut/s is/are made to provide planned hinge-wood and maintain control of tree
6) Cutting technique is adjusted in response to movement and condition of tree
7) Wedges are used to control movement and direction of falling
8) Falling is completed once initiated
9) Planned escape route is used when tree starts to fall
10) Fall of tree and movement on ground are monitored until tree is stable
11) Trees which hang-up are identified and cleared as soon as practicable to meet local codes of practice

Range of variables

- Trees are those of any size, species and condition which can be safely fallen
- Falling may require the use of multiple back cuts and/or boring techniques
- Falling will be undertaken in all conditions for which it is safe including slopes up to a maximum allowed by relevant regulations
- General factors and site hazards identified includes trees to be felled and retained, extraction methods, processing location and environmental care principles
- Environmental requirements include those relating to gullies, water courses and seed and habitat trees
- Visual assessment of tree covers size, weight distribution, lean, species, multiple leaders, soundness of timber, growth characteristics and stresses
- Clearance for assessment and provision of escape route may require assistance from dozer or other machine
- Work is to be undertaken with general guidance on specific worksite, coupe/compartment and environmental requirements

- OHS regulations include Codes of Practice and SA2727 and requirements include carrying of correct first aid kit, erection of warning signs, wearing of required personal protection including head, eye, ear, cut-proof leg protection, safety footwear and high visibility vest, manual handling requirements, maintenance of safe forest practices including location of other people and potential falling objects, required actions relating to forest fire, working alone requirements, recognition of hazards and required actions in bush and tree falling and use of approved containers for fuel and oil

Evidence guide

Underpinning knowledge

Explains:

- OHS regulations, policies and procedures for the manual falling of trees
- All safety and environmental requirements for operation in forest settings
- Limitations in conditions and trees for falling
- Process of assessment, planning and falling for the range of trees and conditions including techniques for control of falling direction consistent with this range
- Planning related to worksite requirements and extraction methods
- The preparation and communication which maintains efficient falling
- The importance of accuracy
- The purpose of record keeping

Underpinning skills

Demonstrates the ability to:

- Safely and effectively operate chainsaw equipment and material over the full range of processes for the manual felling of trees
- Locate, interpret and apply relevant information in written, diagrammatic and/or oral form
- Convey information in written and/or oral form
- Interpret and apply common industry terminology
- Apply safety and environmental requirements for operation in forest settings
- Assess, plan and fall within the range of variables for trees and conditions including techniques for control of falling direction consistent with this range
- Plan work to site requirements and extraction methods
- Prepare and communicate to maintain efficient falling

Critical aspects of evidence

Assessment must confirm the application of appropriate knowledge and skills to:

- Safely harvest trees
- Communicate effectively with others in associated areas
- Apply mathematical procedures such as estimation and measurement
- Access, interpret, assess and apply technical information
- Plan falling sequence
- Prepare and maintain falling equipment
- Apply environmental protection measures
- Assess tree

- Prepare surrounds
- Fall tree

Independent assessment of units
This unit will normally be assessed as a discrete/stand alone competency

Assessment context
This unit may be assessed in the workplace or under conditions which accurately simulate a realistic workplace

Additional reference material

- WorkCover code of practice 2002
  Safety in forest harvesting operations
- WorkCover guide 2001
  Risk management at work
- Contractors safety pack 2002 State Forests of NSW
- AS 2727 – 1997
  Chainsaws – Guide to safe working practices
- AS 2726.1 – 2004
  Chainsaws – Safety requirements for general use
- AS 2726.2 – 2004
  Chainsaws – Safety requirements for tree service
- AS/NZS 4453.1 – 1997
  Protective clothing for users of hand-held chainsaws
  Part 1 Protective leg wear
- AS 2210.1 – 1994
  Occupational protective footwear –
  Guide to selection, care & use
- AS/NZS 1801 – 1997 & Amdt 1.-1999
  Occupational protective helmets
- AS/NZS 1336 – 1997 & Amdt 1.-1997
  Recommended practice for occupation eye protection
- AS/NZS 2161.1 – 2000
  Occupational protection groves – selection, use & maintenance
- AS/NZS 1270 – 2002
  Acoustics – hearing protectors